RICH SEAMS

by Kenneth Wood

Manchester Geological
and Mining Society
1838–1988

ISBN No. 0 904905 13 6

150TH ANNIVERSARY
MANCHESTER GEOLOGICAL
AND MINING SOCIETY
1838 – 1988

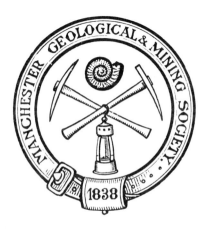

"To investigate the Mineral Structure and
Organic remains of the Earth, to inquire
into the statistics and machinery of
mining, to collect books, sections, maps,
models and mining records, to publish the
Transactions of the society with suitable
illustrations, and to form a museum to be
open gratuitously to the public."
Objects of the Society, 1838.

Contents

The Future of Coal

by Sir Robert Haslam, BSc, CEng, HonFIMinE
Chairman, British Coal Corporation

Sir Robert Haslam

The first industrial revolution, when Britain became the workshop of the world, was founded on coal. In more recent times - particularly during the years of public ownership since 1947 - the coal industry has no longer been a monopoly fuel supplier in Britain. The competition comes not only from oil, gas and electricity generated by nuclear power, but also from internationally traded coal from low-cost producer countries.

However, in the fiercely competitive business environment the industry now faces, coal retains a significant role as Britain's biggest single source of energy, representing during the year 1986-87 over one-third of the nation's total energy consumption. By our efforts we are winning the confidence of customers, in industry and in homes, to buy British coal. We have to convince them, by our continuing achievements that they are right to stay with us.

In particular this means fully realising the considerable potential of the mining systems and highly capitalised equipment installed at our modernised and new mines throughout the coalfields. Modern machine mining is "light years" removed from the pick-and-shovel hand-got methods which were commonplace when I began my career in the mid-1940s in the Lancashire coalfield, and where I qualified for my colliery manager's certificate in 1947. I joined the Manchester Geological and Mining Society in 1944 as a student and much benefitted from my early involvement in the Society during my formative days in the industry.

Conditions in the heavily faulted Lancashire coalfield have always tested the skill and ingenuity of mining engineers, and it has been a very good training ground for potential managers. A significant contribution has been made to the advancement and the mechanisation of coal mining by former illustrious members of the Manchester Geological and Mining Society - particularly James Anderton, the Lancashire mining engineer who invented the Anderton shearer-loader. The industry has benefitted from their great pioneering work.

On colliery visits since rejoining the industry as Chairman of British Coal, I have been enormously impressed by the advances made in mining technology and equipment. These have not only increased productivity but have also significantly improved safety, which will remain a dominating priority in all our operations.

Following underground visits to the Bickershaw Complex and other collieries in all the major coalfields, I have no doubt that we are pursuing the right strategy - improving performance by concentrating on faces with optimum potential and ensuring that heavy duty equipment is extended to virtually all of them during the next four years.

Impressive advances have been made in labour productivity, and these must continue. However, the greatest challenge we face is to improve our capital productivity. Mining in Britain is a highly capitalised activity and it is essential to get the maximum return on the substantial investment which has been made. Flexible working arrangements and coal mining operations on more than five days a week are needed for the industry to survive and to prosper in the increasingly competitive energy climate.

Members of Manchester Geological and Mining Society realistically recognise that, in scale, they will have a diminished role in the years ahead, compared with the expansive operations of the Lancashire and Cheshire coalfield in the past. I have no doubt, however, that their skills and commitment will be needed even to a greater extent in the future, to help ensure the industry's success in the highly competitive business environment which will take us towards the 21st century and beyond.

Rebuilding the New from the Old

by Mr K. Moses, FEng, FIMinE, FIMEMME, FRSA, FBIM
Vice-President of the Institution of
Mining Engineers

"We have the technology", is a much used phrase now commonly acknowledged as meaning rebuilding the new from the old. The British coal mining industry can justifiably say it has practised "the art" throughout its history.

Over the years the mining engineer has been forced to examine and progressively develop equipment and techniques to overcome the constraints placed upon him by the environment in which he needs to produce coal safely to meet market requirements.

Technological development in the industry has been, in the main, evolutionary rather than revolutionary, but there have been some significant steps, perhaps the most notable since nationalisation being the development of the Anderton Shearer Loader. A more detailed record is given in this historical review, but it was James Anderton, a significant personality in the industry and the Manchester Geological and Mining Society, who, by combining basic engineering principles and older devices, sought to develop what is today the principal machine used for winning coal.

The evolution of the shearer brought with it a continuing requirement to develop ancillary equipment without which it could not function effectively. Powered roof supports and chainless haulage are further examples of this innovatory approach.

As new technology has been introduced, so too have new hazards. While it has not always been possible to foresee and guard against these, the application of technology itself, by way of protective and monitoring devices, has helped the industry to become the safest in the world today.

What is the future for technology? Deriving the full benefits of the mechanisation programme of the 1950s and 1960s understandably took some time as there was a need for continued innovation in design to meet the varying conditions encountered. The next major technological contribution will come from the use of the microprocessor, the potential capabilities of which have yet to be fully realised.

I believe the most significant factor in the future will be to harness the technology we have developed to seek improvements in machine reliability and better utilisation of the capital invested in our collieries. We must obtain the full potential of the many years experience which has enabled the British longwall coal mining industry to become the most advanced in the world.

It is this hard earned experience, admirably recorded in the transactions of the professional institutions associated with the industry, that will serve to help keep it at the forefront of mining technology.

This history of the Manchester Geological and Mining Society, of which I had the honour of being President in 1970-71, is indicative of the industry's ability to survive and continually "rebuild the new from the old".

Preface

by Dr. Michael B. Jones, BSc (Hons) Mining, CEng, FIMinE
President of the Manchester Geological
and Mining Society Branch
and H.M. Chief Inspector of Mines and Quarries

It is a privilege to write a preface to this account of 150 years of the Society.

Mining engineers and historians will be indebted to those who have painstakingly pieced together the fragmented records to produce an interesting account of an important period in mining history.

A particular theme which stands out, is the effort made by its members to promote safe working practices in a coalfield which faced, and continues to face, most of the hazards associated with working coal. It is therefore not surprising that mine safety features so prominently in its proceedings. I am particularly pleased to note that Joseph Dickinson, one of Her Majesty's Inspectors of Mines, played such a prominent part in the proceedings of the Society.

I therefore commend this history of the Society to all in the industry and others who have an interest in mining safety.

Forward

Since the Manchester Geological Society was founded in 1838, coalmining, and to a lesser extent the extraction of other minerals, has played a dominant role in its affairs. In the Society's first session, papers were read on the "Lancashire and Cheshire Coalfield" and the "Origin of Coal and the Geological Conditions Under Which It Was Produced." In the years following, the many aspects of coalmining were to be major topics at the Society's meetings, with important lectures being given by eminent geologists and mining engineers.

In 1904 the Society acknowledged that it owed its existence primarily to the coal industry and extended its title to become the Manchester Geological and Mining Society. A year later the Society affiliated to the Institution of Mining Engineers (I.Min.E) and membership was later to become restricted to those with professional qualifications.

For more than 80 years since then, the Society, whose lifespan coincides with the rise and decline of the Lancashire and Cheshire Coalfield, has endeavoured to be at the forefront of advancing technology. Conditions in the industry today have little in common with those prevailing in the 19th century, and this is due in no small measure to the pursuit of geological knowledge and sound mining techniques by members of the MGMS and other mining institutions.

It is for these reasons that the following pages dwell almost entirely on coalmining and, reluctantly, ignore most of the geological papers recorded in the Society's Transactions. Short profiles have been included of some of the early pioneers, and others who played major roles in the development of the Society. Many men who, over the years, contributed learned papers on a wide variety of subjects, have had to be omitted only for reasons of space and time. This is not in any way to belittle their endeavours and, hopefully, in the future their efforts will receive the recognition they deserve.

A major force in the growth of the Society has been the intense curiosity its members have shown for the world they lived in and the strata they exploited. For 150 years the papers read to the Society have been vast in range, impressive in content and often opened the way into new fields.

A valuable record of papers read to the Society is contained in the Transactions, and a small number of papers has been included at the end of this history. The titles have been chosen to reflect the state of knowledge at the time the papers were read, or to give an indication of the ability of the contributor. Apart from the Transactions the other major source of information has been the invaluable Minute Books of the Council, the Society's management committee. Other documentary evidence is sparse, and much has been lost or jettisoned over the years. As a result there are a number of broken threads in the story of the Society.

Following reorganisation within the I.Min.E. in 1972, the Manchester Geological and Mining Society was technically dissolved, and re-emerged as the Manchester Geological and Mining Society Branch of the Institution of Mining Engineers.

With only a small number of collieries now working the Lancashire coal measures, the branch can only look forward to a diminished future, but it can look back on a long and successful past.

CHAPTER ONE

1838: The Foundation

M anchester in the third decade of the nineteenth century was a growing town of fast-developing industry and commerce, with its fortunes based on coal and cotton. The Duke of Bridgewater's canal and the new railways had brought cheap supplies of coal to power the steam-driven mills in which spinning mules had increased output to meet the demands from a burgeoning industrial society.

Scientific thought in the town was dominated by John Dalton, father of the atomic theory and modern chemistry. Dalton's influence was widespread and his students included men who were yet to make their reputations in a number of disciplines. Overshadowing intellectual life was the Manchester Literary and Philosophical Society (the "Lit and Phil") founded in 1781. For many years Dalton was its president and on his death in 1844, another distinguished physicist, James Prescott Joule, son of a Salford master brewer, succeeded him.

Another focal point was the role played by the professional classes such as bankers, lawyers and engineers. By 1838 progressive citizens had become patrons of the emerging scientific and artistic communities and were able to stimulate and support new societies which sought to inquire into social and industrial development.

A society for the Promotion of Natural History, with which the Manchester Geological Society was to have a stormy relationship, was founded in 1823. In the same year the Royal Manchester Institution was established "to diffuse a taste for the fine arts, by establishing a collection of the best models that can be obtained in painting and sculpture." This society was later to become the City Art Gallery in Mosley Street. The Royal Medical School was founded in 1824, and a seat of self-improvement, the Mechanics Institute, which was to evolve into the College of Technology, held its first meeting in 1825. The Athaeneum (1835) offered its members moral and intellectual improvement and later built an imposing home for its activities next to the City Art Gallery.

The 1830s were also to see the foundation of two societies of quite specific interests. The Manchester Statistical Society came into being in 1834 to carry out social and economic investigations into town life, and in 1838 came the inaugural meeting of the Manchester Geological Society. The early history of the MGS mirrors the growth of scientific progress in Manchester. From modest beginnings, and led by practical enthusiasts who were generally self-taught in the science, the Society was to influence the development of geological and mining studies. On the fringe of this serious activity, was the Phrenological Society, which for a short time in 1839 rented rooms from the Geological Society, and which claimed the doubtful science of judging mental ability by the shape of the skull. A plaster cast of Samuel Crompton's death mask was subjected to this indignity after he died in 1827.

The more learned societies benefitted from cross-fertilisation of membership, with founders of the MGS also having their names on the rolls of other institutes. Edward William Binney, soon to become one of the Geological Society's most influential members, had read papers to the Literary and Philosophical Society. Binney also became an eminent president of the Lit and Phil and was to be considered by that society as "a man of much influence....from the force of his personality and commonsense, and from the extent of his geological knowledge." Dr. W. Crawford Williamson, of the Lit and Phil and first professor of Natural Science at Owens College, was also a member of the MGS, as were James Hayward and Mark Philips of the Athaeneum. Hayward and William Langton of the MGS were also founders of the Statistical Society.

Many, if not all of the learned societies, had their own libraries, but by 1825 the Manchester Circulating Library (established in 1765) could boast 12,000 volumes. Subscribers could also use the College Library, The Portico, a law library, the New Circulating Library (1792) and a number of libraries attached to religious institutions.

The key to Manchester's success as an industrial centre lay in its closeness to the Lancashire Coalfield. Even before 1700 demand for coal exceeded that available from the Bradford district and before the Bridgewater Canal was built, fuel had to be hauled over rough roads from Worsley and Clifton. The rapid growth of industrialisation is shown by the increase in Lancashire coal production over a 15-year period. In 1815 the coalfield, extending from St. Helens in the west to Oldham in the east, produced an estimated 2.8 million tons, but by 1830 output had risen to an estimated 4 million tons. Demand for coal was such in 1838 that mine owners were sinking deeper shafts in the search for new seams and this brought increasing technical difficulties. Water pumping became a critical issue and problems with faults in strata brought a challenge for geologists and mining engineers.

The science of geology was still concerned with basic principles but William Smith (1769-1839), with his Principle of Superposition and

Law of Strata Identified by Fossils, had laid the foundations of modern geology and provided knowledge vital to the extraction of minerals from the earth.

The still-young Industrial Revolution was to raise production in factories and foundries to unheard of levels and it was to be achieved against a background of the mining of coal and a growing knowledge of the region's geological structure. It was in this environment of increasing scientific awareness and the region's thriving industries that in 1838 a group of men met in Manchester to discuss the formation of a geological society.

The Manchester Geological Society was to play a significant role in Lancashire's future.

The Friends of Geology

Lord Francis Egerton was the most distinguished of the men who attended a "numerous meeting of persons friendly to the establishment of a geological society" at the York Hotel in King Street, Manchester, on October 15, 1838. Preliminary consultations about forming a geological society had created great interest and those who went to the meeting were generally well-to-do men, established in business and professional life. They were men, too, who felt a strong sense of public duty and responsibility and for whom geology had great appeal.

One attraction the new science held was that no great body of knowledge existed and the talented amateur could, and did, contribute much valuable work at the forefront of an exciting new field. On the practical side there was a growing need for geological research. The Industrial Revolution would literally have run out of steam without the discovery of new coal seams and deposits of iron ore and other valuable minerals.

Almost certainly, one of the prime movers behind the first meeting of the MGS was the young E.W. Binney, a lawyer by training and student of geology by inclination. Binney was to make himself a highly respected reputation both in the Manchester Geological Society and the Manchester Literary and Philosophical Society, becoming President of both organisations. In adopting a name for the Society the inaugural meeting pondered on whether including Manchester in the name might appear to limit its sphere of interest. One proposal suggested a wider ranging title, but Binney later said that if it had been named the "Lancashire, Yorkshire, Cheshire and Derbyshire Geological Society" that letters and papers would not easily have reached their proper destination. "It was called the Manchester

Geological Society for the purpose of giving it a habitat where it might be found," said Binney in his 1865 Presidential Address.

Apart from the flurry of interest in the name of the Society, there seems to have been little else of dispute at that first meeting and a number of resolutions concerning the aims and structure of the Society were passed unanimously. Of principle importance were the first two resolutions:

1. "That the importance of the mineral structure of the surrounding district and the increased interest which prevails at the present day in the progress of geology and in the general advancement of science, require the establishment of a Geological Society at Manchester and that the Society be entitled "The Manchester Geological Society".

2. "That the objects of the Manchester Geological Society shall be to investigate the mineral structure and organic remains of the earth, to inquire into the statistics and machinery of mining, to collect books, sections, maps, models and mining records, to publish the Transactions of the Society with suitable illustrations and to form a museum to be opened gratuitously to the public."

Binney, chronicler of much of the Society's early activities, was later to list an impressive record of achievement which had arisen from the implementation of these resolutions.

The first meeting also set subscriptions at £1 a year with those able to subscribe £10 being offered life membership. Those who did not join the Society at the meeting would later have to find a proposer and seconder before being admitted. These subscriptions were not high enough to fund the Society's ambitions and it is unfortunate that some important papers read in the early years were omitted from the Transactions because of lack of money.

These problems though were far from the minds of those first members and in a spirit of convivial companionship it was decided to hold a dinner twelve months hence on the occasion of the first annual general meeting.

Much work had gone into organising the inaugural meeting and it cannot have been coincidence that there were present enough men to fill all the offices of the first Council. Lord Francis Egerton, a very powerful man in the new industrial society, was elected President. Apart from his interests in the Bridgewater Trust, Egerton was a man of many other parts. He had inherited an income of £90,000 a year from his uncle, the Duke of Bridgewater, and was able to display generosity towards causes he favoured. He supported "men of genius" and at his London home a gallery of magnificent paintings was open to the public. He also had valuable connections in the world of politics. The Member of Parliament for South Lancashire, his career in government included appointments as the Lord-Lieutenant of Ireland, Secretary of War and, briefly, a Lord of the Treasury. He advocated liberal-conservative policies, a "wet" in today's language, and had strong views in support of free trade. It was almost certainly his interest in the sciences which led Egerton to attend the inaugural meeting of the MGS. When the British Association for the Advancement of Science held its annual meeting in Manchester in 1842, Egerton was President, and he also had long connections with the Royal Geographical Society.

The first Council elected by the MGS was:
President: Lord Francis Egerton
Vice-presidents: Sir Philip de Grey Egerton, Dr Fleming, Samuel Haywood F.G.S., and Mark Philips MP
Treasurer: Mr William Langton
Auditors: Mr. S.E. Cottam and Mr. P.M. Jones
Secretaries: Mr. Thomas Ashworth and Mr. H.C. Campbell
Ordinary members of Council: Mr. Ainsworth, Mr. William Fairbairn, Mr. John Barker, Mr. Robert Grundy, Mr. Watson Beever, Mr Thomas Kirkham Junior, Mr. E.W. Binney, Mr. H. Lees, Dr. James Black, Mr. John Leigh, Mr. Thomas Boothman, Dr. Lyon, Mr. J.E. Bowman, Mr. R. Mann, Mr. M. Davie, Mr. William Ross, and Mr. G.S. Fereday Smith
The last item on the agenda at the meeting elected John Dalton, then in failing health, as an honorary member.

Pioneers of 1838

An outstanding personality in the Manchester Geological Society in its first 30 years was Edward William Binney, who gained an international reputation in geology as an authority on the Lancashire coal measures. Apart from a wealth of material Binney left in the records of both the Geological Society and the Manchester Literary and Philosophical Society, his son, James Binney, wrote a memoir in 1912 on the centenary of his father's birth.

This booklet provides insights into Binney as a man of scientific ability and also claims that Binney may have had some influence on the political efforts of Lord Ashley (later Lord Shaftesbury) which led to legislation banning women and children from working underground in mines.

Binney was born at Morton, near Gainsborough in Lincolnshire on December 7th, 1812, the seventh son of nine children. "I came to trouble the world," he said in later years. At seven he went to Gainsborough Grammar School, run by a Dr. James Cox, "one of the hardest birchers ever known." The young Binney excelled at history and geography but was reluctant to progress at mathematics and seems to have shown no great interest in geology in his school years. Probably the only minerals he saw as a child were gypsum, embedded in red marl in the school playground, and traces of cornelian and agates found in the ballast used to repair roads. When Binney left school at 16 he wanted to study chemistry, but his elder brother, Mordecai, introduced him instead to the law, and in 1828 Binney was articled to a solicitor in Chesterfield in the heart of the Derbyshire Coalfield, an area which provided a ready field for scientific research.

Binney was already "a child of nature" and enjoyed roaming the countryside studying bird and animal life. In his teenage years Binney's interest in geology began to unfold and he began to collect fossil shells and plants from the tips around coal and ironstone mines.

E. W. Binney

He also made friends of mining agents, including John Gratton, author of the Geological Map of the Derbyshire Coalfields and Working Collieries. Binney, said his son, acquired most of his knowledge from natural sources rather than studying books. It was in Chesterfield that the teenage Binney first came across seatearth, or crow-stone as it was known locally, the fossil earth on which rest the coal seams. He observed that the stone was full of stigmaria ficoides, which an old miner told him were the roots of plants. This was later to be a topic on which Binney was to do a great deal of research and become the subject of important papers.

In Chesterfield Binney became involved in politics and wrote "squibs" for Figaro, a local paper. He so annoyed a number of local worthies, including his employer, that he was refused a reference for a new position in Hereford. Instead he went to London for two impecunious years and although geology does not seem to have been a prominent part of his life while in the capital, he did seize the opportunity to inspect sections in cuttings being made for the new railways.

Binney decided to seek his fortune in Manchester and in July, 1835, he arrived in the city without a friend or introduction. He set up chambers in Spring Gardens and lodged in Cooper street, opposite the Mechanics Institute, which he joined to take advantage of attending the lectures and using the library. In his leisure time in those early years Binney became a close friend of Doctor John Leigh, physician's clerk at the Royal Infirmary, and regularly accompanied him on his rounds visiting patients. While on one of these Sunday morning strolls Binney noticed a culvert being cut on land at Newtown. "Some of the materials thrown out by the excavation were lying near the road. They were red marls, and he split some of them with his knife and found plenty of casts of shells in them." These were later to be identified as Gervillia Bakewellia, but at the time of discovery Binney had never seen or heard of them before and the following day both he and Leigh returned to collect more specimens. Two labourers were hired at a cost of some £5 to dig down into the marl and then sink a borehole for a further ten yards.

In 1835 Binney and Leigh read a paper to the Manchester Literary and Philosophical Society on their findings, and later they also wrote a paper on the fossils for the London Geological Society. Their discovery also impressed the young W. Crawford Williamson, then the curator of the Natural History Society, and he helped Binney and Leigh identify the strata indicated by the fossils. In his book, "Reminiscences of a Yorkshire Naturalist," Williamson names the most important fossil found as Schizodus Obscurus.

Binney's early geological knowledge was based on much personal observation, and James Binney claimed that in the first five years of his residence in Manchester his father had walked "many thousands of miles" around the city. This strong inclination towards the natural sciences, his study of the Lancashire Coalfield, and his close acquaintance with students of Dalton and the engineer William Fairbairn, was to make Binney, at the age of 25, a prominent founder of the Manchester Geological Society.

According to his son, Binney's role in the Royal Commission into the Employment of Women and Children began in 1840 when Binney was spending an evening with Joseph Brotherton, MP for Salford, who together with Lord Ashley was then attempting to get the Commission launched. Binney apparently suggested to Brotherton, who was

Chairman of the House of Commons Private Bills Committee, that the coal industry should be be included in the inquiry. Binney, together with Francis Looney, another stalwart of the Manchester Geological Society, organised a petition to the House of Commons in favour of the Commission. They obtained sketches of women hauling skips of coal underground and these were also said to have been exhibited at Westminster.

In support of this family memory of Binney's role in the Royal Commission, are the facts that Brotherton was a staunch supporter of the Factory Acts and Ashley had social contacts in Manchester. Ashley's "earliest and truest" friend was Lady Egerton, wife of the President of the Geological Society, and he was also a friend of Sir James Kay-Shuttleworth, educationist, member of Manchester Statistical Society, and later to be President of the Manchester Geological Society. When Looney died in 1855, the Manchester Guardian credited him with being "instrumental in calling the attention of the legislature to the employment of women in coalmines, and he used his most strenuous endeavours to prevent them being employed as beasts of burden underground."

Binney was challenged some years after the 1842 Act banned children under 12 and women from working underground, by a woman still working in the mines. While near Ince Hall Colliery, Wigan, Binney met a woman who bemoaned that since the Act was passed employers would only run the risk of allowing women to work underground if they were paid 3s a week less than before. "She wished that people would mind their own affairs, and not interfere where they were not wanted unless those gentlemen who caused the law to be passed, would make up the difference of her pay," wrote Binney's son. Copies of Binney's papers on his efforts to alleviate conditions for women and children in mines were sent in 1876 to Mr. A. Macdonald, MP for Stafford.

A long-standing advocate of mine safety, Binney apparently also experimented with a design for a miner's safety lamp which was only "tolerably successful." No details of the lamp appear to have survived.

Binney was a prolific contributor to the Manchester Geological Society and between 1839 and 1872 he delivered 33 papers. The origin of coal was a question which exercised considerable discussion amongst those early geologists and one of Binney's major contributions, the proof that coal seams are situated directly above fossil soils, came as a result of the observations he first made at the age of 16. Traces of roots in seatearth "show that those soils supported a luxuriant vegetation (sigillaria), which growing rapidly in vast swamps, under a moist atmosphere of high temperature, formed by decomposition the fossil fuel, to which we owe the extent of our manufacturing industries," wrote a biographer after Binney's death in 1881. The lawyer's knowledge of the geological structure of the Manchester area and specialised interest in the coalfields, also proved invaluable when the Geological Survey was made.

Binney's skills as a lawyer made him a fortune from the infant coal-oil industry. In 1845 he won a case involving patent infringement for James "Paraffin" Young, the Scots-born entrepreneurial chemist, and they were to be friends and partners for many profitable years. In 1850 Young patented a method of distilling lubricating and lamp oils from coal, and together with Binney, and a third partner, Edward Meldrum, founded a business at Bathgate, near Edinburgh. For 14 years the partners ran the business until the patent ran out and one estimate claimed they made £600,000 profit (some £18m by today's values) after paying all expenses. With an income on this scale, Binney bought colliery interests in Scotland and a private estate in the Isle of Man, and yet still maintained a strong interest in geological research.

Binney felt an affinity for other amateurs who pursued scientific truths, but whose purses did not match their intellectual ambitions, and in 1843 he was an active promoter of the Society for the Relief and Encouragement of Scientific Men in humble life, which provided funds for impoverished researchers. He also sprang to the aid of Samuel Gibson of Hebden Bridge, a whitesmith by trade, but whose spare hours had been devoted to the study of botany and geology.

Respected in scientific circles, Gibson's work on fossil shells from the lower coal measures was presented to the Geological Society in its first session, together with exquisite drawings by Captain Thomas Brown. In later years Gibson fell on hard times and was forced to sell much of his lifetime's collection, including valuable boxes of insects which were bought by a clergyman for one shilling a box. Binney was angry when he heard of the meagre price paid by the clergyman, and asked him to sell them back at the same price so the specimens could be re-sold. The clergyman refused until pressure was applied by Professor Adam Sedgwick, and the boxes were later auctioned in Manchester for £45, twenty times the price originally paid. Binney wrote to the clergyman, who was not named, saying that the man of the cloth would no doubt be delighted to know how mistaken he had been over the value of the specimens. There was no reply.

Men of Science

Together with Binney at the inaugural meeting of the Manchester Geological Society were other notable people involved in the scientific and commercial life of the city. A brief review of some of those first members shows how extensive and intertwined were their interests.

JAMES PRESCOTT JOULE (1818-1889) was probably the most outstanding student to be taught by John Dalton, although their tutorial association lasted only from 1835 to 1837 when Dalton suffered a stroke. The son of a wealthy Salford brewer, Joule had a room in his father's house converted into a laboratory where he carried out experiments which led to his first paper, "On an electro-magnetic Engine," being published in 1838. This was followed by creative work in physics which led to Joule's name being counted amongst the greatest in science. By all accounts an unassuming man, Joule was a personal friend of Binney, and they were elected to the Lit and Phil on the same day. Joule remained a member of the Geological Society for many years, and despite the demands on his time and energy he was a Secretary of the Society for a short time.

SIR WILLIAM FAIRBAIRN (1789-1874) started his working life at the Percy Main Colliery in Northumberland, but a talent for mathematics together with mechanical ingenuity were soon to lead him to fame as an engineer. After being appointed to look after the engines at the colliery, he became a friend of George Stephenson, before going to seek his fortune in London and then Manchester. By 1824 he and his partner, James Lillie, had the reputation of building good textile machinery but speculation in a new cotton mill turned sour and the partnership ended. Fairbairn turned to the building of iron ships, before his heavy engineering interests expanded in many directions, including later working with Stephenson on the tubular bridge over the Menai Straits.

An adoptive son of Manchester, Fairbairn spent most of his life in the city and led a circle of associates interested in the sciences. An early advocate of technical education for workers he was one of the founders of the Mechanics Institute and a founder member of the Council of the Geological Society. In a paper he read to the MGS, he urged coalmine owners to adopt an improved version of the Cornish pumping engine which provided great economy in the use of fuel.

SIR BENJAMIN HEYWOOD (1793-1865), a prosperous banker, had played a major role in the foundation of the Mechanics Institute and was a strong advocate of its members pursuing scientific interests. For 20 years he was President of the Institute and as part of his interest in the education of the working classes he encouraged the introduction of certificates of proficiency for students completing a course of study. He was an active founder of the Statistical Society and in 1834 read to the Royal Society the report of an inquiry into the condition of the working class in Manchester.

JAMES HEYWOOD (1810 - 1897), the younger brother of Sir Benjamin Heywood, left the family banking business to pursue an academic and political career. After studying at Cambridge he was called to the bar in 1838 but never practised law. A nonconformist, like his brother, he sat as a Liberal MP for North Lancashire after being returned unopposed in 1847. Geology was a principal interest of the younger Heywood, and in 1837 a paper he read to the British Association at Liverpool, on the Lancashire Coalfield, so impressed Professor Adam Sedgwick that he proposed Heywood for membership of the Royal Society. At the first general meeting of the Manchester Geological Society in January, 1839, Heywood read a paper on the Geology of the Irwell between Clifton and Manchester, and was twice President of the Society. Together with William Langton and Richard Cobden he was one of the founders of the Manchester Athenaeum.

JAMES BLACK, born in Scotland, served as a surgeon in the Royal Navy during the Napoleonic Wars. Retired on half pay, he moved to Bolton to begin a long connection with the north west. His wide-ranging interests included involvement in public health, contributions to medical papers, a paper to the Literary and Philosophical Society on the Roman Garrison of Mancunium, the founding of a free library in Bolton, the presidency in 1842 of the British Medical Associaton ... and membership of the Manchester Geological Soiety to which he read a paper on The Objects and Uses of Geology. He was also President of the MGS from 1851 to 1853.

WILLIAM LANGTON moved to Manchester in 1829 to take up a post as cashier in Heywood's bank. He was a founder of the Manchester Statistical Society, the Manchester and Salford District Provident Society, the Athenaeum, and Owens College.

G.S. FEREDAY SMITH studied mining and geology in Germany, and was also an experienced railway engineer. At the age of 25 he was appointed Deputy Superintendent of the Bridgewater Estates, a position he held for 50 years.

GEORGE WAREING ORMEROD (1810-1891) was by profession a successful lawyer, but his leisure was devoted to geology and he published 29 papers on the subject, including work on the Cheshire saltfield. Born in Tyldesley, near Leigh, he was a long-standing member of the Geological Society, being Curator, Secretary and Treasurer at various times. His brother Henry, was also a long-serving member and official of the Society.

FRANCIS LOONEY was a remarkable man from quite ordinary circumstances. A printer by trade, he was one of the first geologists to specialise in the Lancashire Coalfield. He was also greatly interested in the education of miners and other working people, and lectured on the danger of gas in mines. On his death, the Manchester Guardian credited him with an effective role in the campaign which led to legislation which banned women and children working underground. Looney later earned his living as the secretary of the Manchester Zoological Gardens until they closed, and then as a collector of market tolls before becoming a sub-librarian at the Free Library. His later years, before his death in 1855, were marred by prolonged illness.

CAPTAIN THOMAS BROWN (1785 - 1862) was a life-long enthusiast of the natural sciences and wrote a good many books on varied topics, including birds, dogs, horses and taxidermy. His major preoccupation was conchology, a subject in which he was considered an authority. After serving in the Army, the Scots-born Brown settled in Manchester and did much research in the surrounding areas, occasionally naming finds of fossil shells after friends. In adopting a discipline for the classification of shells he compared a Class with an Army, an Order with a Regiment, and a Species with a Soldier. In 1838 he was appointed as the £150-a-year curator of the Manchester Natural History Society, and was an early member of the Geological Society, of which he became a Secretary and Vice-president. He illustrated much of his own work and drew specimens on one occasion for a paper given to the MGS by Binney, on The Fossil Fishes of the Pendleton Coalfield. When the MGS merged its museum with the geological collection of the NHS, Brown devised a scheme for the re-arrangement of the collections. He became later became involved in a bitter feud with the Geological Society, and in particular with Binney.

JOHN EDDOWES BOWMAN whose early scientific life was devoted to botany, "possessed mental powers in which the calm and philosophical spirit of mature age was united with youthful ardour." He lived for many years in North Wales and studied the Silurian and Cambrian strata, and presented a collection of lower Silurian fossils from the Berwin Mountains to the Society. On moving to Manchester he studied the local measures, and was amongst the first to read papers to the Society. He theorised on the origin of coal and made an important study of fossil trees found in a railway cutting at Dixon Fold on the Bolton-Manchester railway. Shortly before his death in 1841 he worked on the effect of glaciation and sought a solution to the source of the gravel beds and erratic boulders "which have for so long puzzled geologists." In pursuing his work Bowman "admirably displayed his patient investigation and love of fact without regard to pre-conceived hypothesis," said Binney in a tribute after Bowman's death.

Elias Hall

The Manchester Geological Society was to bask in the reflected achievement of famous men of science who accepted invitations to join the Society in an honorary capacity. Dalton, and the geologists Sir Roderick Murchison, Sir Charles Lyell and Sedgwick, were four prominent members of the scientific world who added their names to the honorary roll. Also in that distinguished list, was Elias Hall, born in humble circumstances in Castleton, Derbyshire, but "a venerable man of science well known in Manchester."

Hall, whose work was overtaken by the rapid growth of geological knowledge, was also subjected to ridicule in his lifetime, and spurned by his home village after his death in December, 1853, at the age of 89. Hall was a particularly active and respected honorary member and he read a number of papers and took part in various discussions. In 1839 he gave a two-part paper on "The Great Lancashire Coalfield", and this was followed in 1844 by "The Coalfields of Yorkshire, Derbyshire, Leicestershire, Lancashire and North Wales," and "The Geology of the Valleys extending from Manchester to Bolton and Bury," (1845); "An Exhibition and Description of a model of Derbyshire with an Account of the Various Strata," (1846); and "An Account of the Coalfields of Derbyshire and Yorkshire, illustrated by a geological map and sections" in 1847.

His death passed with little notice, but in 1861, Binney sought to record the achievements of "the father of Lancashire geology," who he said had laboured in the science for upwards of 70 years. Binney told the Society that Hall had been an acquaintance of William Smith and one of Sedgwick's teachers, and had also assisted Farey in the production of "Geology and Agriculture of Derbyshire" published in 1813.

Hall, described by Farey as a "fossilist and petrifaction worker", made a geological model, coloured stratigraphically, of the Derbyshire Peak district and also one of part of the Lake District. Two of the models, pioneering exercises in the then infant theory of superposition of strata, were bought by the British Museum. Hall's work was at first little appreciated by the established authorities and Farey recalled an attempt to humiliate Hall when the models were shown to a London society.

"No sooner was one of his models shown before several of its leaders, than, without waiting to examine a single particle of its laborious details, advantage was taken of an injudicious use of rather too glaring colours in Mr. Hall's first attempt, to raise a laugh by the far-fetched and contemptible joke, that "a tray of guts and garbage in a

15

fishmonger and poulterer's shop", rather than anything else, was called to the mind by viewing this elaborate model of the stratified hills and dales of a tract of country! Such was the conduct of the heads of a Geognostic Society, and such the rewards of meritorious labours..." Hall was made of stern stuff and not a man to be disheartened by a bad joke, said Binney. Hall went on to make a model of the neighbourhood of Manchester which was exhibited in the Museum of the Natural History Society in Peter Street.

Of even greater interest was Hall's work in producing, in 1832, a mineral and geological map of the Lancashire Coalfield, including parts of Yorkshire, Derbyshire and Cheshire. It was probably the first attempt at establishing the geological succession in the area, and although the Geological Survey superseded Hall's work in the succeeding decades, he deserves great credit for his pioneering work. "This labour must have occupied Mr. Hall for many years," said Binney. "The difficulties to be encountered in tracing the coal seams of this extensive district, dislocated and fractured as they are, ever varying in thickness and quality, and covered up sometimes by hundreds of feet of drift deposits, are only to be estimated by those who attempted to investigate a single parish."

Binney admitted there were flaws in Hall's work, but praised his plan of dividing the different coal seams by their accompanying sandstone, which were laid down on the map in different colours. "His bold and vigorous mind has chalked out the broad outline and it remains for young and active geologists...to fill up the details."

A "dear old friend" of Hall's was Professor Williamson of Owens College, who, sixty years after the coalfield map was drawn, acknowledged its great defects but gave Hall the credit for having made the first intelligent attempt to map the strata of Lancashire. "How far he failed you will be able to understand when I tell you that he contrived to intercalate almost in the middle of the coal measures some of those drift sands that we have so abundantly in the neighbourhood of Manchester, particularly on the north side," Williamson told the MGS during a lecture in February, 1892.

After his work on the coalfield, Hall produced a section from the Irish Sea through Lancashire, Derbyshire, Yorkshire, Nottinghamshire and Lincolnshire to the North Sea, which he dedicated to Professor Sedgwick. An introduction to the map was later published with the assistance of Looney, who listed the fossils to be found in the different strata. Hall, described as a man of stern self-reliance and indominatable perseverance, said his map should be received by the public as the mineral is received by the smelter, "with a view to extract the purer metal for his remunerating purposes." He urged those using the map to exercise great caution "lest the ardent imagination of the geologist should lead him into error, by causing him to draw false conclusions." Aware of the need to preserve his own integrity, Hall said that conclusions based on unreliable data would ultimately prejudice the author in the scientific world, and he had abstained from theoretical opinions and used only facts which he had verified by observation.

On his death Hall was buried with little ceremony, and Binney said in 1861 that not even a stone had marked his last resting place. Geological Society members, concerned at this lack of recognition, raised a subscription and suggested that a tablet should be erected inside Castleton church to mark the memory of one of the village's more illustrious sons.

Binney later reported to the MGS that when villagers heard of the plans to put a plaque in the church "quite a hubbub was raised by some of the so-called gentlefolk" who objected to a poor and old man being so honoured. A £10 fee was demanded before a plaque could be installed so the MGS members decided instead to buy a tombstone for Hall's grave. "The gravestone is just as good as the tablet which would have cost ten guineas for permission to put up in the church, even if this privilege could have been obtained for a poor man, without the magnates of the village raising an outcry," said Binney.

Detail from Elias Hall's mineral and geological map of the Lancashire Coalfield.

Alan Davies' collection

CHAPTER TWO

At the Beginning

T here was a great deal of confidence in the air on October 31, 1839, when the Manchester Geological Society held its first annual meeting. Binney, one of the honorary secretaries, Bowman and Hall, had each read two papers to the Society in its first session. There were 130 members on the books and generous donations of £130 had been made. A house in Falkener Street had been rented for meetings and a modest start had been made on both a museum collection and a library. Books purchased included Captain Brown's Fossil Conchology of Great Britain and Clay's Observations on the Ashton Coal Field. A valuable donation included Hall's Geological Map of Lancashire, and specimens from the coal measures together with "a portion of elephant's tusk," had been given to the museum collection.

How little had yet been discovered of geological matters was shown in the proposal by the Geological and Polytechnic Society of the West Riding of Yorkshire which invited the MGS to join them in undertaking to construct a section across the Pennines along the line of the new Manchester to Sheffield railway. "...it will not only throw light on the valuable coal deposits of Denton and Hyde, and the lower part of the coal field, but prove the relation of the latter to the Great Yorkshire Deposit," said the MGS annual report. "The great similarity of the two coal fields leads to the supposition that they were once united, and the investigation of the one will materially throw light on the contents of the other."

A delegation met the Yorkshiremen to discuss the project and to decide on a joint scale of three inches to the mile horizontally, and an inch to fifty feet vertically. Three lines of section from the North Sea to the Irish Sea were proposed, the first being from Aldborough on the east coast, across the Vale of York through the Leeds Coalfield and then via Haslingden and Chorley to a little north of Ormskirk. The second line was from Hedon on the Humber through Swinefleet, Barnsley, Woodhead, Tintwistle, Mottram, Roecross, Stalybridge, Ashton, Audenshaw, Ardwick, Manchester and across the new red sandstone plain to just south of Liverpool. The last suggested section ran from Humberstone, Lincolnshire, through Caister, Bawtry, Tickhill, Chesterfield, Castleton, Macclesfield and across the Cheshire salt deposits to North Wales.

Both the MGS and the Yorkshire society agreed that the second proposal was the best as it would show all the Yorkshire strata on the rise and dip as well as the most productive part of the Lancashire coalfield. The cutting of the Manchester-Sheffield railway would also help with observations. The Manchester Geological Society agreed to survey the country between Manchester and Woodhead, but soon ran into difficulties, particularly between Openshaw and Ashton-under-Lyme, and Roecross and Mottram. In the Autumn of 1840 it was reported that no great progress was being made but a mass of valuable information had been collected. Whether or not that survey was completed is unknown, but already another proposal had been made for a section to be made of the country from Rivington Pike, near Bolton, to Crosby on the Irish Sea.

James Heywood donated prizes of £20 and £10 for the best horizontal sections of the Lancashire, Cheshire and Yorkshire Coalfield. The Society wanted mineowners to allow overlookers to compete as "...such a course is calculated to give a stimulus to men in attaining a correct knowledge of the geological structure of the neighbourhood." The competition was hedged with restrictions and Hall was told that work he submitted was not eligible. After two years the only other two entries were declared void, and there is no evidence that working miners submitted work. With little interest shown in the first competition, the Society then decided to offer the prize for original work on vertical sections in the coal strata. One problem geologists faced in creating sections in those days was the lack of a large-scale map and to overcome this difficulty the Society began a campaign to have the Lancashire Coalfield surveyed on the 6" scale.

The general map in use at that time was the 1" scale but in 1825 the Board of Ordnance had started a 6" survey of Ireland and the maps had impressed geologists and mining engineers with their accuracy and detail. The Council of the Geological Society considered the current maps totally unfit for displaying topographical and geological details of a densely populated manufacturing county "and of valuable coalfields whose dislocations and fractures of small superficial extent, are of so vast importance both to the practical miner and the proprietors of the land." In England and Scotland only a few areas of military importance had been surveyed using a 20" scale, and the Society wrote to the Treasury urging the Government to fund a six-inch survey of the Lancashire Coalfield and surrounding areas.

Despite opposition from private surveyors who thought their incomes may be affected and from a Government trying to reduce public expenditure, Lord Francis Egerton reported at the Society's second annual meeting in October, 1840, that permission to survey

South Lancashire on the 6" scale had been granted and the Master General of the Board of Ordnance said the arguments used in the Society's petition were a principal ground in granting permission. The Master General was also directed to consider any observations the Society may have to offer about matters to be included in the survey, and "the purposes to which it may be desirable to render it subservient." The new survey was soon started and Lancashire, Yorkshire and parts of Scotland were surveyed on the 6" scale between 1840 - 54.

More than 50 years later in October, 1892, the Society again became involved with the Ordnance Survey and asked that the maps be brought up to date, with the inclusion, where absent, of the 25-foot contour line. It was also suggested that to make the Survey more accessible to the public that the price of the maps should be reduced.

The Society was also hoping that coal owners would help geological research by providing details of the strata which they worked. This vain request was to be repeated almost annually for many years and there was great disappointment at the general lack of interest shown by colliery proprietors. The Society, following the lead of similar organisations in other coalfields, wanted to collect books, maps, models, sections and mining records.

In July 1839 the Society sent out 250 letters to Lancashire coal owners appealing for assistance but only received a reply from Ralph Thicknesse, MP, of Wigan. That first circular read:

"We are directed by the Council of the Manchester Geological Society to request the favour of your furnishing them with copies of any notes, of measures gone through in shaft sinkings, particulars of borings, and plans of workings, which you may have in your possession. "Being convinced that much valuable information has been lost to the Coal owners of this and the adjoining Counties owing to the want of a place for the reception of the documents above alluded to, the Society has determined to form a Depository of Mining Records, relating to the Lancashire and Cheshire coalfields; such depository to be kept at the rooms of the society...and to be open to the inspection of members, parties furnishing records, and gentlemen introduced by members. As a collection of sound practical information, conveniently arranged for reference, and readily accessible, cannot but be of the greatest benefit to the mining interests, the Council trusts that the proprietors of Collieries will do all in their power to assist in the formation of a registry of well ascertained facts, which shall not only be of value to the neighbouring Country, but of service to the nation at large.

"The Council will feel further obliged by receiving answers to the accompanying series of questions, signed by the proprietor or overlooker of the mine, and by the presentation of any fossil organic remains, with the names of the places where found, for their Museum....'' The attached questionnaire read:

1. Name and locality of the colliery.
2. Names of the owner of the land and the present occupier of the colliery.
3. Number, names and descriptions of the seams of coal and other minerals it contains.
4. Number and description of the beds or layers of each seam and their respective cleavages.
5. Thickness and quality of the several seams of coal; which of them have been worked - to what extent, and why the working of any of them has been discontinued or not commenced.
6. The system of working.
7. The amount of inclination and direction of the dip of the strata.
8. Direction, character and extent of the faults and the materials they contain.
9. The amount of steam or other power employed in lifting water from the mine, the depth of the pumping, its diameter, and the number of gallons of water raised per hour.
10. Number of shafts, and their diameter and depths.
11. Accidents by explosion, and whether they occurred when the Davy (lamp) was used or not.
12. What other accidents have occurred at the colliery and their causes.
13. The system of ventilation practised.
14. General observations.

Thicknesse replied to most of the questions and included an account of an inquest on a collier killed in an explosion at Kirkless Colliery, Wigan. Binney seems to have been particularly disappointed by the lack of response to the questionnaire but he later agreed that it included many questions which proprietors would not have answered, for fear of supplying information which might bring in a competitor and injure trade.

Another progressive idea in 1840 also came to nothing. The Society appealed to mine and quarry owners to send in two samples of coal or rock, one to be sent to London for analysis and the other to be displayed in Manchester for inspection by customers. Only three members, Ralph Thicknesse, William Peace of Haigh, Wigan and Andrew Ray of Pendleton, sent in specimens, but no doubt if mineowners had shown more interest, it would have added an important industrial and commercial dimension to the Society's activities. As it was the industry had to wait until the advent of the Inspectors of Mines and new legislation before much of the information the Society had requested became necessary under law.

Undaunted by past experiences, the Society made another attempt to approach the coal proprietors in 1858, but again the appeal was largely ignored. In 1893, with the Society then dominated by mining engineers, another attempt was made to secure assistance from the coal owners, with the same dismal results as before.

Despite these reverses the Society did thrive in its early years and in ending its 1839 report, the MGS Council reinforced the importance of having the Society's museum open to the public without payment, an issue which was to bring conflict with the Natural History Society in the years ahead.

Gifts of fossils to the museum were not only beautiful in themselves, concluded the report, but were "the alphabet by which we are enabled to read the state and condition of the globe, long before it was fitted for the habitation of man. Their highest value consists in the evidence they so clearly display, that in those infinitely remote epochs, the Great Author of all things exercised the same power and wisdom in creation, and the same benevolence in providing for the wants of his inferior creatures, as pervades the whole system of the material universe at present."

The museum collection grew rapidly and early contributions came from, amongst others, Sir Philip Egerton (600 Old Red Sandstone specimens), The Marquis of Northampton (Tertiary fossils from Sicily), Ralph Thicknesse, (Fossil coal plants from Kirkless Colliery, Wigan), G. Fereday Smith (two slabs of fossil footprints from the Trias, at Runcorn), T. L. Gooch, the railway engineer (fossils from the Summit Tunnel), William Peace of Wigan (Carboniferous fish remains) and J.E. Bowman (fossils from the Berwin mountains, and four specimens of fossil roots from Dixon Fold, near Manchester). This early list is by no means complete and does not include the Binney collection loaned to the Society. Pride of place in the museum was to be awarded to a magnificent speciment of a ichthyosaurus, found in alum shale near Whitby, and bought for the Society in 1847 by James Heywood and George Hadfield, MP.

In 1842 the Society came into the public eye when the British Association for the Advancement of Science held its annual meeting in Manchester. Binney, reporting on the success of the event, told a meeting of the Society: "In no town has this useful Association gathered together a more distinguished assemblage of illustrious philosophers, or blest the world with more valuable contributions to knowledge. Amongst the section rooms filled with some of the most celebrated men of the day and their attentive listeners, it was gratifying to find that not one was more crowded than that appropriated to Geology, evidence showing that the science is making good progress."

Geological studies within the Society continued with some members in 1843 working on the "superficial deposits which envelop nearly the whole of the counties of Lancaster and Chester, so long termed diluvium, but now better known as drift." Determining the structure of the drift was not only valuable to farmers, but also to builders, brickmakers and shaft sinkers. It was also anticipated it would give information on the source of the water which flooded mines.

In 1845 there was a flurry of excitement at the October meeting when a Mr. Rhodes presented a specimen from the Carboniferous grits of Tintwistle. A vote of thanks was made to the finder "for his great labour, care and attention in bringing the impressions...before the Society and in presenting same to the Society."

The interest aroused by Rhodes' specimen came from "impressions popularly supposed to be of human feet." The Society voted to send the specimen to London for inspection, as soon as the Manchester members had made their own examinations. A note pencilled in the margin of the minutes for November 10, 1845, also states that a paper was read on "The footsteps from Tintwistle." The Geological Society in London, with rather more scepticism, declined to examine the find.

Rhodes' discovery does seem to have survived to this day. In Salford Mining Museum there is a large slab of rock bearing two faded inscriptions which state: "Presented by the Council of the Geological Society, Manchester", and "Impressions in millstone grit from Tintwistle". A recent scientific note alongside the specimen says: "Block of millstone grit from Tintwistle showing footprints of a large amphibian (Chelichnus Ingens) which lived in the Carboniferous 345 million to 280 million years ago. The block shows one complete footprint in the centre ...with deep heel impressions, one in front of the main footprint, the other to the upper right. The other marks are the result of natural weathering. The animal probably made the footprints in wet sand which subsequently solidified in to a rock bed and so preserved them."

How the rock arrived in Salford, and to whom it was presented, is not known, and even though Rhodes was wrong in his conclusions, he did at least know there was something unusual in what he had observed. And that is a neccessity for scientific progress.

Moving on

In the first few years of its life, the Society had a number of premises and the first meetings were held in St. Ann Street in a building owned by Heywoods, the bankers. After a brief spell in Falkener Street the Society moved to more spacious rooms in James Heywood's home in Mosley Street and in 1842 the Society moved to the Royal Institution where they stayed until 1851.

The mid-1840s proved to be a critical time for the MGS, with Binney becoming estranged from its activities, and a decline setting in which was to come perilously close to ending the Society's existence. Binney was involved in two issues which led to him becoming less involved in the Society. One of these affairs is recorded but the origin of the other, which was to rumble on for almost 20 years, is as yet a mystery.

In the early summer of 1844 the Society's museum was visited by the King of Saxony, who was presented with a copy of the Transactions by G.W. Ormerod. Binney was in the museum at the time of the visit and Ormerod apparently suggested to a royal aide that the Society's Secretary should also be introduced to the King. The Royal visitor declined to meet anyone else, and Binney, greatly annoyed, appears to have threatened to resign over what he saw as a slight, not by the King, but by a fellow member of the Society. A complaint was lodged against Ormerod who profusely regretted any misunderstanding which might have led to Binney not shaking the royal hand. "It is ... most earnestly hoped that Mr Binney will be induced to continue his most valuable services to this Society," the anxious Council recorded in the minutes in July, 1844.

Binney was not to be appeased and in August, 1844, resigned as Secretary. Nor was he appointed to the Council at the annual meeting in November, but the following year he did gain a place. In 1846 Binney, together with five other Council members, had "to go out agreeably" from the Council under the Society's rules, and not for some time did this founder member take an active part in the Society's activities. Following Binney's resignation as Secretary his place was taken by Captain Brown.

In October, 1847, Binney wrote to the Society saying he wanted to remove his collection from the museum, and the Council ordered that his fossils be catalogued. The Society, wishing to keep the collection, made certain proposals to Binney and in December, 1847, he wrote agreeing, but added: "You must excuse me meeting your secretary, Captain Brown, on the subject of my fossils as I must respectfully decline to hold any communication with him." This enmity was to continue until Brown's death in 1862. The Society responded equally

25

vigorously to Binney's ultimatum, and sent him a copy of a resolution which read, "That Manchester Geological Society decline to communicate with Mr. Binney except through their regular officers," and as Binney refused to meet one of their secretaries they would not further their proposals on the future of his fossil collection.

The reasons for Binney's quarrel with Brown are not known, but certainly from the time of the origin of the dispute and with Binney no longer active in the Society, momentum was lost and the Society's fortunes went into serious decline.

In the later 1840s meetings were regularly cancelled for lack of support, and at the annual meeting in October, 1848, the Council lamented that members were failing to support the objects of the Society. "Small attendances which now take place cannot be but mortifying to those who have expended both time and trouble, and frequently expense, in laying highly valuable information before this Society," said the annual report. A declining membership and a number of members in arrears with subscriptions had also brought financial pressure on the Society by early 1849. By October, 1849, the Council was complaining that few papers had been read and attendances had continued to fall away, and "from the smallness in number of those who attend no practical benefits can result to geology." At that year's annual meeting a committee was established to reorganise the Society's affairs.

By February, 1850, matters had become quite critical and a rule was amended so that in the event of the Society being dissolved, its remaining funds would be given towards the promotion and encouragement of geology and natural science. In early June a special meeting was called to discuss the future of the Society and amongst the 17 members attending was Binney. A resolution that the Society be dissolved as speedily as possible was amended, and yet another committee was set up to "confer with the Manchester Natural History Society and any other body...as to the terms upon which this Society can be best accomodated."

In October, 1850, the Geological Society approached the Manchester Literary and Philosophical Society, Salford Borough Royal Museum, the Natural History Society and the Mayor of Manchester, asking if any of them would accept the Society's library and museum in the event of dissolution. With the request was sent a long list of questions asking about facilities. The Lit and Phil would only accept the library, but the Salford Borough Royal Museum was enthusiastic about accepting both. The NHS declined to answer the questions and no reply at all was received from the Mayor. Still struggling to retain its identity, the Geological Society then decided to ask the "Lit and Phil" and the NHS if either of them would offer accomodation for the library, museum and a meeting room. By the end of November, 1850, terms had been agreed with the NHS, which had its own premises in Peter Street, Manchester, but which itself was also showing signs of decline.

The agreement provided for the merging of the Geological Society's museum with the geological collection of the NHS. Admittance to the joint collection would be free to the public, and each society would appoint two honorary curators, one of whom was to be Binney, to manage the geological museum. The NHS museum would still make a charge for visitors. The NHS also offered accomodation for the Geological Society library, a free meeting room, and two seats on its Council for members of the MGS.

In June, 1851, the Geological Society left its rooms at the Royal Institution and moved to Peter Street, the scene of a remarkable and long-running episode in the Society's history.

CHAPTER THREE

The Troubled Years

Moving the Manchester Geological Society museum and library from the Royal Institution to the Natural History premises in Peter Street, Manchester, was not complete until 1853. In the meantime meetings of the MGS were being held there, but the fortunes of the Geological Society were now at their lowest ebb. No ordinary meetings were held in 1853 and 1854 and for the next six years only a handful of members, including Binney and Brown, kept the Society going.

There is evidence of disagreement between the Geological Society and the Natural History Society as early as 1854, when Henry M. Ormerod, one of two honorary museum curators appointed by the MGS, wrote a letter complaining that the NHS had not followed procedure in allowing a specimen to be loaned from the geological collection. The NHS replied that they had authority under their own constitution, an answer which did not satisfy Ormerod who went on to draft a compromise which involved consultation with the four honorary curators. In 1855 Ormerod resigned as curator and was replaced by Binney.

Manchester Geological Society, founded in such a wave of enthusiasm and high hopes, was now struggling to survive. By the winter of 1854-55 attendances even at Council meetings had reached pitiful levels with some meetings being abandoned for lack of a quorum. The meeting of September, 1855, was attended by only three stalwarts, James Heywood, Henry M. Ormerod, and Captain Brown. The minutes of that meeting are brief and without explanation, but the following resolution was passed:

"That the following circular be issued by the Secretary, having obtained the sanction of twelve members.

"On the requisition of twelve members of the Manchester Geological Society, we do hereby summon two special general meetings of the Society to be held at the rooms of the Manchester Natural History Society, in Peter Street, in the City of Manchester; the first on Tuesday the 13th day of November next, and the second on Tuesday the 15th day of January next, at 11 o'clock in the forenoon of each day; at which two meetings it will be proposed absolutely to dissolve the Society, and to transfer or dispose of the Library, Funds and all the other property of the Society, in such manner as the said two meetings shall think fit; and also to decide on the undertaking to be given by the Manchester Natural History Society for the purposes and in the manner described by Rule 33 of the Manchester Geological Society."

"Resolved that the General Annual Meeting of this Society be summoned for Thursday the 25th next...and that a special meeting of the Council be summoned for Thursday the 18th next."

Quite what precipitated these resolutions is not known, but possibly they arose from a sense of frustration by the small group of members who had attended meetings in recent years, and who felt it would be better to dissolve the Society rather than see it limp into oblivion.

The two meetings called by the resolutions are also something of a mystery. The Council meeting on October 18 was attended by Binney, Ormerod, Bowman and Brown, who, according to the minutes, merely admitted Thomas Black as a new member and confirmed the minutes of the previous meeting. At the annual meeting on October, 25, 1855, Samuel Walker was in the chair and the only other members present were Joule, Bowman, Ormerod, Binney and Brown. Normal business followed, with accounts being presented, curators making reports, and officers and members of Council elected.

Neither in the minutes of the meeting on October 18, or the annual meeting on October 25, is there any mention of the ultimatum to close the Society. It may be that the ultimatum played the part it was intended and created a resurgence of interest in the Society, for by the meeting of December 11, 1855, ten new members were admitted. This new blood included several mining engineers: William Peace of Haigh, Wigan; Elias Dorning of Manchester, and George Peace of Ashton. Also admitted was Sir James Kay-Shuttleworth, pioneer of working class education, a founder member of Manchester Statistical Society, and a prominent voice in Manchester's intellectual society. It was also at about this time that Joseph Dickinson, Inspector of Mines, was invited into the Society to give authority to its mining activities.

Binney played an important role in putting new life into the Society, and at a special meeting on December 18, 1855, he read a lengthy paper on the Objects of the Manchester Geological Society. In anticipation of a growing membership, 250 copies of the Society's rules were also ordered.

Over the next few years many new members were to be associated with the mining industry, but stimulating interest in the Society's regular activities was to be a recurring problem. In

November, 1860, Binney proposed that meetings should also be held in the evening, rather than during the day as was usual, and this would help to attract younger members and others not practically acquainted with geology.

The Penny Umbrella Stand

The first real evidence of soured relations bewteen the two societies came in May, 1859, when the Geological Society Council ordered a letter to be sent to the NHS Council "complaining of the conduct of Captain Thomas Brown in attempting to dissuade persons from becoming members of the Geological Society.

"Also that the Council of the Geological Society having been informed that a charge for umbrellas is intended to be made on persons visiting the Geological Museum beg to refer the Natural History Society to the rules...which stipulate that the Geological Museum be open gratuitously to the public."

The issue of the Penny Umbrella Stand, although trivial in itself, threatened the Geological Society's principle of having its museum open free to the public. The NHS was accused of trying to impose admission charges when it proposed to the geologists that everyone entering the geological rooms would have to leave their umbrellas or walking sticks before entering, and pay a fee of one penny. The NHS already imposed an admission charge on visitors to its own museum.

It was not a particularly clever subterfuge by the NHS and the geologists agreed to the matter being discussed between a member of each society, who ruled:

1. That the NHS is entitled to order all the umbrellas and sticks to be deposited before entering the room.
2. That the NHS was not entitled to make a charge for people depositing umbrellas or sticks, who were solely visiting the geological collection.
3. That the Geological Society should provide a proper receptacle to be placed in the Geological room on which it should be stated that the articles were left at the owner's risk, but that their safety could be insured on the payment of one penny.

An item in the balance sheet of the NHS for 1861 shows that visitors to the NHS museum paid £139.14s.10d in admission fees for the year, and that £4.16s.4d. was received for umbrella charges.

One small touch of humour from this unhappy period was recalled by Joseph Dickinson almost 40 years later at the MGS 60th Anniversary, when memories were recalled of "Old Parker", collector and assistant curator of the NHS. In the mid-1850s, with the Geological

Society at a low ebb, a meeting had been called to discuss its future. Only three MGS members and James Parker had turned up, and they were close to being outnumbered by newspaper reporters covering the meeting.

Not wanting to broadcast the plight of the Society, Dickinson said the Press were good enough to put the best face on it, "for in describing the attendance they spoke of Captain Brown, presiding, and (amongst others present), were Mr Binney, Mr Dickinson etc.' Mr Parker being the etcetera."

Skirmish of the Keys

Generally at this time relations between the two societies were poor and the MGS set up a committee to look into the matter. In November, 1859, began the Skirmish of the Keys, after Binney reported to the annual meeting that the NHS had taken possession of the keys to MGS specimen cases and prevented the geological curators from doing their work.

The management of the joint collection, said Binney, rested with the four honorary curators, two from each Society. Since the transfer of the geological collection to the Natural History Society premises, the united collection had been in the care of the honorary geology curators, for, said Binney, "the Natural History Society took little notice of it and did little or no work."

Two keys for the display cases had been placed in a locked box kept on a window ledge. During Ormerod's time as a curator, Brown had been refused his own key to the cases because he was a paid curator of the NHS, and the rules stated that the management of the united collection should be entrusted only to the four honorary curators. In May 1859, Brown, with the support of a resolution of the NHS, wrote to the Geological Society demanding that a key be handed over to him "and if refused, that keys be provided." James Parker, with whom Binney had left the key to the locked box, was then summoned before the Council of the Natural History Society and persuaded to hand it over.

Worse was to come in this saga of inter-society rivalry. The NHS honorary curators claimed the keys to the specimen cases had now been stolen, and without consulting members of the Geological Society had put new locks on the display cases. "It is difficult to imagine what could be the object of the peremptory demand of the keys of the geological collection except to cause a quarrel," said Binney.

Even though Brown had once been refused a key he had forced the lock on the box in which the case keys were kept and had had a copy made "some years since," Binney added. At the Geological Society annual meeting in October he urged the Council to take swift action to rectify the state of affairs. He also repeatedly asked in vain for the NHS honorary curators, Dr. James Braid and Dr. Ashton, to return his key.

The dispute moved into the public domain when a report of the MGS annual meeting was printed in the Manchester Courier. Dr. Braid replied to the charges against the NHS in a long letter to the Courier in which he put the blame for the whole dispute on to Binney's shoulders. The NHS demand for a key, said Braid, was consistent with his Society's rules. "It was evident to the (NHS) council that Mr Binney's contumacious conduct in refusing to give up the keys of the Geological Society into the custody of Captain Brown...was intended as an insult to our Council as well as Captain Brown," wrote Braid. Braid claimed that in an exchange of letters, Binney had said he would not condescend to ask Brown for the master key taken from Parker, and that when Brown discovered that the case keys had been stolen he was both astonished and perplexed. Braid also claimed that Binney had shown no interest in the theft of the keys and so Braid had decided to have all the case locks changed.

"The Council of the Geological Society ... would have it (the theft) appear a mere trick or juggle to get Captain Brown made custodier, but a more absurd idea would not enter the mind of man, seeing that he already had been confirmed keeper of the keys by the NHS Council. Yet in the face of all this, Binney had the rudeness and audacity to impute the theft to myself and Captain Brown., charging us before our Council with a conspiracy to get the keys into Captain Brown's custody, but it must be obvious that it could hardly be expected that a sane man should utter such an absurdity," added the Doctor. With a final sting in the tail, the letter said the Geological Society should appoint a new curator in place of Binney. As for the theft of the keys, Braid said it remained a mystery.

At their next meeting the geologists resolved to retain their dignity and ignore the letter, many statements of which were claimed to be totally unfounded. They did make their point of view known however by sending copies of their resolution to the Editor of the Courier and the Council of the NHS. The MGS Council also supported Binney and said that Braid had broken open the case to the keys, and was guilty of a breach of his society's rights, and that Geological Society officers had the right of access to their collection at all times. The NHS Council replied by passing a resolution praising Braid for his action over the keys, and said in a letter to the Geological Society that the geologists never had a right to the custody of the keys to the united collection and the NHS did not consider they had infringed the terms of the union.

The affair rumbled on for more than a year with the geologists having no access to their cases. The NHS refused arbitration and in one note to the MGS said a letter they had written "respecting the conduct of Mr. Binney" had not been answered. The geologists' distinguished President, Sir James Kay-Shuttleworth, reported in December, 1860, that he had met Brown and told him that some resolutions of the NHS were "a palpable usurpation of power on their part." Brown was unyielding and Sir James said he found him "utterly impracticable and altogether unreasonable."

It was the British Association for the Advancement of Science which brought the warring societies to an uneasy truce. The British Association was holding its annual meeting in Manchester in 1861, and requested the loan of geological exhibits for display. In May 1861 the MGS Council wrote to the Natural History Society asking them to join the geologists "to take means to have the fossils etc., of the geological collection (currently secure behind NHS locks) cleaned, named and arranged." The NHS eventually agreed to meet half of the £40 cost of cleaning the collection and "...that the keys to the geological collection be placed in a box to be fixed in some secure situation, and that pass-keys be entrusted to the curators of both societies".

With the MGS geological collection "again in proper custody", the Society's curators appealed for the addition of more coal measure fossils to make the collection "one of the first in the country". Attention also needed to be paid to the addition of Lancashire Silurian, Permian, Triassic and Pleistocene specimens.

Both Captain Brown, before his imminent death, and Binney, were to suffer further indignities. Brown was not re-elected to the Geological Society Council and was listed only as a member ex-officio. Brown died in 1862 before the issue of the keys finally ended and it reflects the bitterness between the two societies that in March, 1863, the MGS wrote to the NHS complaining that "a great number of copies, in sheets, of the Transactions of the Manchester Geological Society, have lately been bought by a waste paper dealer at the residence of the late Captain Thos. Brown, having been improperly removed there from the museum - and to request them (NHS) to take means to prevent any more of the property of this Society (MGS) from being disposed of by the representatives of the late curator." The MGS also wrote to Brown's daughter informing her of the resolution.

Binney, a MGS representative on the Council of the Natural History Society, was not invited to a Council meeting in 1863 and was told he would not be welcome until he apologised for intemperate remarks made at an NHS meeting in 1859. The dreary affair finally ended when the two secretaries of the Geological Society, but not Binney, wrote to the NHS saying "We are authorised to say that Mr.Binney - under the belief that an approbrious epithet was applied to him at your council meeting, unchecked by the Chairman of the meeting - added words which otherwise he would not have done." The date of that letter was July, 1863, ten years since the societies had their first brush.

Relations between the societies were not to improve overmuch with sniping continuing on various subjects. A lasting solution though was closer than perhaps some members of the Geological Society might have realised. The Natural History Society had been in decline for some time and in 1861 its annual report sought to dispel "certain reports lately current regarding the financial standing of the Society," and repeated a statement from the previous year's report "that there is no intention whatever of handing over this collection to the Corporation of Manchester." In 1864, with the Geological Society enjoying better fortunes, the NHS was now looking for a white knight to save it from extinction, and despite their stance of three years earlier, decided to negotiate with the City of Manchester "with a view to arranging for the transfer of its institution...as a free museum." Over the previous ten years the NHS had spent little on new specimens and the condition of the collection had declined. Free public museums, particularly the one in Peel Park, Salford, had reduced the number of paying visitors.

The NHS was willing to offer the city its collections, together with the valuable property in Peter Street, in exchange for a pledge to continue the museum and the study of natural history in Manchester. The Geological Society had not been forgotten and the NHS chairman, Murray Gladstone, hoped it would agree to a proposal aimed at preserving a public collection under scientific guarantee.

The proposal was to be adopted within a year or two, but with a different suitor, Owens College, which was then embarking on an expansion scheme which would eventually lead to the establishment of the University of Manchester. In April 1867 the MGS received an approach from Owens College asking about the possibility of its geological and minerological collection being deposited at the College. The Council thought discussions would be premature but by November a Special Committee was set up to investigate the offer "under circumstances arising from the course of action adopted by the the Natural History Society," which had agreed that its collection should be endowed as a public museum as part of the Owens College extension.

The Special Committee, resolute in its obstinacy towards anything to do with the NHS, refused to discuss a letter in February, 1868, because it had been addressed only to the MGS Council. A month later the letter had filtered through the Geological Society's system, and the Special Committee agreed to receive written proposals or to attend a conference with the Commissioners of Owens College about the future of the geological collection. A resolution from the Natural History Society then gave the MGS notice that its collection could stay in the Peter Street building only until the NHS museum was moved to Owens. In January, 1869, a long report on the proposed transfer, with safeguards on free public admission to the museum, was received from the MGS Special Committee.

These prevarications by the geologists apparently so annoyed their own President, G.C. Greenwell, that he wrote: "I regret much an engagement near Leeds will prevent me from attending the meeting of the Manchester Geological Society tomorrow. I regret this the more on account of certain exceptional points that have been raised, which from the spirit in which they seem to be taken up cannot add to the respectability and influence of the Society. And which therefore ought to be summarily disposed of. I am at the same time, satisfied that unless a more liberal feeling is introduced into the MGS it must collapse.

This reprimand from a senior member had some effect and the Council was authorised to negotiate with Owens and report back "with such alterations and improvements as they think fit." In September, 1869, a special meeting approved an agreement with Owens College and the geological collection was transferred, to join the natural history museum of the defunct NHS, in what was to become renowned as the Manchester Museum. One member of the Geological Society keeping an interested eye on the negotiations over the transfer of the collection was W. Boyd Dawkins, curator of the Manchester Museum, and later a prominent geologist.

Following the demise of the Natural History Society, its premises were run by the Commissioners of the Owens College Extension who allowed the MGS to remain in Peter Street until the building was required for other purposes. That stay of execution lasted until 1873 when the Geological Society moved into rooms in the Literary and Philosophical Society premises where they stayed for more than 20 amicable years.

So came to an end a long and unhappy episode in the Society's history. Greenwell deplored that in 1869 little had been done to promote the objects of the Society, and only one paper had been read.

Thankfully it was a situation which was to rapidly improve, but memories of this unhappy time lingered on and even twenty years later, on the 50th anniversary of the Society, the Council reported that the agreement with the NHS had been "subject to a good deal of disagreement, misunderstanding and discomfort."

Better Days

After the turbulent years in association with the Natural History Society, the affairs of the Manchester Geological Society settled down to more mundane matters in their new home in George Street. The next major issues were to be the changing of the name of the Society to include mining interests (1904) , and federation with the Institution of Mining Engineers (1905). Before then there were many papers to be read, a large number of them based on experiences in the Lancashire coal industry.

Copies of the Society's Transactions were in great demand and exchanges were made with societies in Europe and America. In December 1886 the Society received a letter from Dr. W.G. Black, a member of the MGS living in Edinburgh, who suggested that the scientific interest of the Society would be enhanced from the admission of meteorological subjects into the programme of papers, and that the MGS be promoted as covering "geology and its allied science meteorology and their application to mining, metallurgy and water supplies." Black's suggestion was apparently partly based on the daily readings of atmospheric pressure taken in the coalfield as part of the precautions to warn when firedamp might be more likely issue from the strata into the workings. On days of low pressure gas escaped more freely from the seams than on days of high pressure. No action was taken on the letter, and a year later a request from the Scottish Meteorological Society asking for aid for its Ben Nevis observatory was also ignored.

At the Society's 50th annual meeting in 1888 it was reported that "...the peaceful and prosperous progress of the Society, to judge from the last 15 years, is established." The Society continued to keep a careful eye on the Geological Collection in the Manchester Museum, now in a new building in Oxford Road, to ensure that the agreement on opening hours for the public was maintained. In 1887 the British Association asked the Society to take up some definite work in connection with one of the Association's committees, and a small number of members began a survey on the distribution of erratic boulders in the area, a field explored by J.E. Bowman almost 50 years earlier.

The 1890s were to be important in the history of the Society with the first serious negotiations taking place over federation with the Institution of Mining Engineers and a search for new premises. An interesting purchase for the library made in June, 1893, was a manuscript by Elias Hall of a geological section of the coal measures between Manchester and Derbyshire. The Society paid £2 for the historic document. In the spring of 1895 the Literary and Philosophical Society needed more space for its library and required the rooms rented to the MGS which was given notice to quit. Unlike the long arguments when tenants of the Natural History Society, the MGS had a long and amicable relationship with the Lit and Phil. By the autumn of 1895 the MGS had found new rooms in John Dalton Street which they initially shared with the Association of Architects.

CHAPTER FOUR

Change of Name
and Federation

Manchester Geological Society's records show that by the early
1860s the number of coalmining members was increasing
steadily and engineers were playing a growing role in the
Society's affairs. In 1861-62, 27 new members were enrolled and 13 of
them gave only collieries as their addresses. No doubt amongst other of
the out-of-town members there would also be men engaged in the coal
trade. It was at this time that a change in the Society's emphasis was
mooted to reflect the growing influence of mining.

The annual report for 1861 says "... in a discussion at one of the
ordinary meetings held some time ago mention was made of the
desirableness of making the Society more of a Mining Institute than a
Geological Society, the improvement of mining being one of the objects
of the Society. As such a prospect may appear feasible to many persons,
it has been thought right to draw the attention of members to the
subject and commend it to their consideration."

No progress appears to have been made and it was not until 20
years later in October, 1881, that the matter was again discussed briefly
and dismissed quickly. A Mr. Tonge suggested at the annual meeting
that the words "And Mining Institute" should be added to the name of
the Society. Joseph Dickinson said that although the Society's main
strength was amongst its mining members rather than pure geologists,
the title had been adopted because it was concise, and he doubted the
wisdom of change. Leader Williams was afraid a change might be taken
for a sign of weakness - trying to make the Society look younger than it
was. There the matter rested for another decade, but by the early 1890s
outside pressures and a threat to membership began to be felt.

In September, 1891, Manchester Geological Society agreed to
subscribe to the Federated Association (sic) of Mining Engineers. In the
November of that year "in anticipation of a meeting of the Federated
Institution of Mining Engineers in Manchester" the following
February, the Geological Society delegated Messrs Burrows, Bramall,
Cockson, Dickinson, Ridyard, Jas. Tonge, Winstanley and Saint "to
carry out the necessary arrangements" and allocated £10 to meet

First crest   *Amended crest*

incidental expenses. From these modest beginnings began a long courtship which 12 years later was to lead to the MGS becoming a federated member of the Institution of Mining Engineers, and a final acknowledgement that the Society was totally committed to the furtherance of coalmining.

A sign of the the way the Society was to go came in 1903 when a vote to change the name of the Society to the "Manchester Geological and Mining Society" was carried without protest. The change appears to have arisen quite casually following discussion at a Council meeting in December, 1902, of a suggestion that a West of England Mining Institute should be founded. Henry Hall, President of the Society, suggested that if the words "and Mining" were added to the name of the Manchester Geological Society, it might both increase membership and subscription income. It was decided to ballot members on the suggestion, and without any recorded dissension the change was agreed. By September, 1903, a new crest, incorporating the ammonite of the 1838 crest, together with crossed miners' picks and a safety lamp, had been designed.

Federation

By 1894 strong pressure was growing for federation with the Institution of Mining Engineers then based in Newcastle-upon-Tyne. The Federated Institution, founded in 1889, had six member societies covering all the coalfields in Britain, apart from Lancashire and South Wales. The major advantage of federation for mining members of MGS would be that papers read at meetings of other societies would be printed in the Institution's Transactions and made easily available. The majority, if not all, of these papers would be on mining technical matters, and would provided a valuable source of information on advances in the industry.

The first overtures for federation came in the autumn of 1893 and were to lead to a degree of conflict between the geological members of MGS and the mining engineer members. It was also to lead to the resignation as Secretary of Mark Stirrup, who strongly opposed federation.

At a MGS Council meeting on November 14th, 1893, there was a long discussion on a letter received from Walton Brown, Secretary of the Federated Institution, following a conversation Brown had had with Joseph Dickinson. It was decided to circularise and ballot MGS members to an opinion on federation.

Mark Stirrup, as Secretary, prepared a letter which clearly showed his opposition to the proposal. Stirrup briefly dismissed the advantage of MGS members receiving a copy of all the publications of the federated societies, and then listed the disadvantages:

- That the distance of Newcastle-upon-Tyne from Manchester would render it impossible for MGS to be adequately represented on the Council of the Federated Institution.
- The Federated Council might refuse to print MGS geological papers in their Engineering Memoirs.
- The printing of MGS Transactions would be removed from Manchester to Newcastle.
- The organisation of the MGS would be gravely injured.

A postcard was enclosed with Stirrup's letter so that members could register a vote. At a special Council meeting on December 1, 1893, Stirrup carried the day when it was revealed that the voting was:

For Federation	24
Against Federation	84
For further consideration	3
Not classified	6
Resignations	6

The mining engineering lobby did not accept this reversal and despite the vote the Society President, William Saint, was asked to draw up a report on federation. Five weeks later Saint presented a strong case in favour of federation, and forecast a gloomy future for the MGS if it were not carried. Saint said the Federated Institution of Mining Engineers was founded in 1889 for "the advancement and encouragement of the science of mining, metallurgy, engineering and their allied industries" and for obtaining a more general recognition of the importance and value of the profession of a mining engineer.

In 1893 the Federated Institution had 2,060 members and was

comprised of the Chesterfield and Midland Counties Institution of Engineers, the Midland Institute of Mining, Civil and Mechanical Engineers, the Mining Institute of Scotland, the North of England Institute of Mining and Mechanical Engineers, the North Staffordshire Institute of Mining and Mechanical Engineers, and the South Staffordshire and East Worcestershire Institute of Mining Engineers.

Walton Brown had told Saint that a scheme had evolved which preserved the corporate identity of each member society, while giving a means of communication on technical matters between the various Institutions. The proceedings of each member society were published in the Transactions of the Federated Institution. If there was agreement on federation MGS would retain its local independence and keep full control of its possessions and proceedings with the exception of future publications.

It was the question of corporate individuality which was to lead to the foundering of the 1894 talks. Rules 1 and 2 of the Federated Institution mentioned advancement of mining, metallurgy and engineering but was silent on geology, said Saint. Rule 8 said that if required by the Institution, a member society should have Ordinary members, Associate members, and Honorary members. There was no provision for geologists except as Honorary members. Rule 41 of the Institution, referring to publications, did not include geology as a specific subject for papers.

Saint was confident that despite the rules, geologists had been admitted as Associate members and that geological papers were an important feature of the Institution. "...the omission of geologists and geology from the rules...are admitted to be defects which can be remedied if the MGS decides to join," the report continued. Saint recommended that provided the bye-laws of the Institution were amended to include geology as one of its objects, the general scheme would be "admirably adapted to the objects of the (Manchester Geological) Society and in that case it could...be allied to the Federated Institution of Mining Engineers with mutual advantage."

The Geological Society in 1894 had 223 members - 202 Ordinary members, 9 Life members and 12 Honorary members. Of the Ordinary members 184 were involved in mining, and 48 were already members of the Institution. Manchester Geological Society had only 18 geologists as Ordinary members. Unless the Society became federated, said Saint, it was probable that a large number of members would resign and join one of the other federated societies. If the MGS declined to join there were plans to establish a Mining Institution for Lancashire and District, which would become federated and which would attract members from the MGS and also affect the influence of MGS. "...The question to be determined," said Saint, "is whether we can continue to stand alone successfully."

Saint's report was circulated to all members and Professor Boyd Dawkins was asked to draw up a letter to the Federated Institution asking if they would amend their bye-law to recognise the status of geologists. On the 30th of January, the Geological Society wrote to the Federated Institution saying they were prepared to discuss federation provided the Institution would amend its rules in favour of MGS geological members.

Stirrup, who had been ill and unable to attend the meeting, disagreed and immediately resigned as Secretary. The MGS Council, reluctant to lose an important officer, twice tried to get him to change his mind, but he remained adamant. Stirrup was later to be made an Honorary member, and installed as President in 1896-97.

Stirrup was a valued member of the Society and had given many papers, including a number on glacial geology and erratic boulders. He had also studied the coalfields and lectured on fossil remains in the coal measures, safety lamps and the effect of atmospheric pressure on firedamp. His other geological interests were wide ranging and included the effect of marine erosion and paleozoic insect fauna. He represented the Society at several British Association meetings and travelled abroad to attend meetings of the International Congress of Geologists.

Over the next few months there was much discussion on federation and deputations travelled between Manchester and Newcastle to negotiate. Another obstacle to federation arose over the question of copyright of papers printed in the Institution's Transactions. The Institution insisted on holding the copyright of papers in the transactions, but MGS members were reluctant to to give up the right.

After a visit to Manchester by the Institution's President and Secretary it was reported that another problem they foresaw was that if Institution rules were amended to included geology then this could open the doors to federation of societies with no mining interests. The Institution would be prepared to admit all the current members of MGS and would, in future, admit geologists with an interest in mining. William Saint, John S. Burrows and James Tonge, who met the two officers of the Institution, suggested in October, 1894, that MGS members again be canvassed for their opinions.

The matter was allowed to rest for three months until Walton Brown again wrote to the MGS who replied, quite briefly, in January, 1895, that because the status of the geological members could not be sufficiently recognised by the Institution that the entire matter of federation was closed...for the present.

It was to be 10 years before the question of federation was resolved and when it was it occurred with no apparent dissent, even though Stirrup was still a member of the Society. The MGS minutes briefly record that in March 1904 a special meeting was called to again discuss federation and to ask for terms and conditions. Mr. A. Drury Mitton hoped "that some action will be taken to give Lancashire mining men a chance to become federated to the Institute." A resolution was passed stating "It is desirable that the Society should become federated with the Institute of Mining Engineers and that enquiries should be made in order to ascertain whether satisfactory terms can be made."

In April 1904 a sub-committee consisting of G.H.Hollingworth, John Gerrard, Drury Mitton, and Saint, was set up to make a report, which turned out to be strongly in favour of federation, and whose contents closely followed the report made 10 years earlier by Saint. To overcome the previous arguments against federation it was suggested that MGS members who did not wish to become members of the Institution would retain all their rights as ordinary members of the Society and would continue to receive MGS Transactions. The question of members retaining copyright on papers read to the Society was solved by a pledge to have them, if neccessary, printed for the MGS Transactions only.

The sub-committee's report said that MGS membership had become stagnant and some Lancashire mining engineers had already joined the Institution through other associated societies and thus denied MGS of potential members. The importance was stressed of MGS members receiving the combined Transactions of the federated societies and it was felt that the Federated Institution was now "admirably adapted to the objects of the Manchester Geological Society."

A ballot of the 224 Society members was held and at a meeting on May 10, 1904, the votes of the 125 members who returned papers were declared as:

In favour of federation	120
Against federation	3
No opinion	2

Hollingworth, President of the Society, was immediately instructed to "take the neccessary steps to effect the desired object; namely: the federation of the Society with the Institution of Mining Engineers." On June 14, 1904, it was reported that the Society's application to join the Federation had been accepted. Five members resigned that month but the Society's membership now totalled 171 federated members and 88 non-federated members.

As a result of federation the membership was divided into Ordinary Members, Associate Members, Honorary Members and "Associates and Students." An Ordinary Member had to be more than 23 years old, and have been trained as a mining, metallurgical or mechanical engineer and have had at least two years experience in a responsible position. An engineer without normal training had to have practised as an engineer for at least five years.

Associate Members were those who were interested in or connected with mining, metallurgy or engineering, but did not practice as engineers. Underviewers, under-managers or others in subordinate positions in mining, metallurgy or other branches of engineering could qualify as Associates, while Student membership was confined to men under 25 years of age who were studying for the profession of mining, metallurgical, or mechanical engineer, or other branch of engineering. An Honorary Member had to "be a person who has distinguished himself by his literary or scientific attainments, or who may have made important communications to any of the Federated Institutes."

In 1906, two years after federation, the Institution of Mining Engineers elected Sir Lees Knowles as its President and held its annual three-day meeting in Manchester. Amongst papers read was one on "The Leading Features of the Lancashire Coalfield", by the venerable Joseph Dickinson, and various day trips were also organised for delegates. One tour went by train to Tyldesley station, near Manchester, from where the engineers walked to Chanters Colliery, owned by Atherton Collieries, and there inspected surface installations. Another journey by tram and train took them to Wigan for a visit to Douglas Bank Colliery.

Delegates who chose the second tour had the privilege of a private tram which took them to New Moss Colliery, Audenshaw, and then on to Ringley Power Station. A third option was for delegates to descend Pendleton Colliery, near Manchester, then the deepest in Britain.

Shortly before his death in July, 1907, Stirrup was to have his early fears about federation realised. In February, 1907, he read a paper on Old and New Geology to the MGS which was turned down for publication in the Federation's Transactions. He suffered a double blow when the MGS also refused to publish it because it had been produced elsewhere as a pamphlet.

CHAPTER FIVE

The Second 75 years

With Federation accomplished, the MGMS moved easily into the role of a professional body for mining engineers, and from 1905 to the present day the Minutes, on the whole, are concerned with the organisation of the Society's affairs. There are however recorded some interesting footnotes to history.

In February, 1910, a young electrical engineer, Arthur Whitten Brown, gave a paper to the Society on "An Empirical Method of Determining the Maximum Output of a Vertical Shaft, using a Cylindrical-drum Winder, under given conditions." Brown, born in 1886 and a graduate of the college which was to become the University of Manchester Institute of Science and Technology, had worked for Westinghouse in Trafford Park, Manchester, and helped design electric winding engines for a South Wales Colliery. The month after his paper was read there was a lively discussion on its contents with fellow Society members. There his reputation might have rested but for an event which ten years later turned Brown into an international hero.

On June 15, 1919, Brown, and a fellow Mancunian, Captain John W. Alcock landed their Vickers Vimy bomber in an Irish bog after a long and dangerous flight from St. John's, Newfoundland, to become the first men to fly the Atlantic non-stop. Both men were to be knighted for their heroic flight and the Manchester Geological and Mining Society joined in the acclaim and sent a message of congratulation to Brown, the plane's navigator. Six months after the flight Alcock was killed in an air crash. Brown never flew again, and went to work for Westinghouse in South Wales.

Apart from the Minutes and Transactions, little now appears to remain of the Society's correspondence and other papers from 1839 to quite modern times and this is partly due to the permission given to the Honorary Secretary by the Council in July, 1918, to destroy, at his discretion, documents prior to the First World War. The Minutes now leave many loose ends, with committees being set up to pursue various matters and no conclusions or reports later included.

Many matters, both administrative and executive, absorbed the Council. In 1911 the Council had to take steps to impose conditions of service on its apparently wayward Assistant Secretary, a paid employee. His hours were to be 9.30 am to 5.30pm from Monday to Friday and 9.30 am to 1pm on Saturdays. The Society also claimed first call on his services and ordered him not to undertake outside engagements in working hours without permission. Amongst other items he was also instructed to obey the Honorary Secretary and keep the petty cash book up to date. All this proved too much for the unfortunate man and he resigned. His successor was appointed later at a salary of £70 a year.

Despite it being more than 40 years since the Society's museum had been transferred to Owens College, now the University of Manchester, a paternalistic feeling for the museum still existed. In 1911 an appeal fund was launched to build an extension to the museum and many MGMS members contributed. Donations ranged from £500 from Professor Boyd Dawkins, to £10 from Lord Lilford, and £3 from Joseph Dickinson, and the total raised by the Society was £1,015.2s.9d.

On the outbreak of the First World War the Society was flourishing, and the position of Honorary Secretary had become too demanding for Sydney A. Smith, who tendered his resignation in September, 1914. Membership then stood at a record 383, compared to 189 in 1905, and Smith estimated that in the previous two years he had written an estimated 2,000 letters on Society business as well as carrying out other administrative duties.

The Great War

First mention of the Great War is made in the Minutes in October, 1914, when H.E. Masswan was sent a letter explaining why his name, proposed in June, had been withdrawn from the ballot list for membership. Masswan, apparently resident in Britain, had German nationality. In January, 1915, with anti-German feeling in Britain running high, Gustavus Ferdinand Bletzger informed the Society that he had changed his surname to Bonner. The Society eventually delayed a decision on his application to have his diploma altered until the War ended.

Members who had enlisted had their names inscribed on a roll of honour which was displayed in the Society's rooms, and subscriptions for volunteers could be suspended for the duration of the war providing the members "could give good reason for such financial assistance." In practice it seems that all applications were granted. The Society's first casualties were reported in June, 1915, with the death in the Dardanelles of Captain Hargreaves Bolton. A month later the deaths of Captain Hugh Brocklehurst Pilkington, Lieut. George S. James and Sapper W.H. Murray, were also reported from the same campaign. On the Western Front miners were used to tunnel under

German trenches and detonate vast amounts of explosives. A member of the Society, Lieut. Ernest J. Philips, serving in such a Royal Engineers tunnelling company, was killed in action in the late autumn of 1917.

The Society's Assistant Secretary, a Mr. Tomlinson, responded to a patriotic appeal for volunteers by Lord Derby, and enlisted. The Council agreed to give him an allowance of 10s a week while he was in the army and to keep his job open. Tomlinson was called up in January, 1917, but two months later the minute referring to his allowance and job was rescinded without recording whether or not Tomlinson had become a casualty.

A curiously worded minute from a meeting in May, 1917, raised the question of "members who may be placed in some difficulty through being called up for military service" and suggested that a note be put in the notice of meetings asking such members to contact the Honorary Secretary so that the Council would be able to ask neighbouring members to offer assistance.

In October, 1915, Sir Thomas H. Holland reported that an advisory council had been formed to advise the Privy Council on scientific research likely to be of industrial value. He thought that a paper on the problems of the Lancashire coalfield might be the basis for urging the Government to carry out a new geological survey of the county. An approach was made to the Lancashire and Cheshire Coalowners Association without success, but the Society did set up a committee to study the proposal, the report of which does not appear to have been recorded.

Royal Charter

The Institution of Mining Engineers played an important role in raising the qualifications and status of mining engineers. In 1913 the Institution made an appeal for a capital fund of £15,000 to give it the financial status to seek a Royal Charter. Each of the seven federated institutes agreed to raise a share with the Manchester Geological and Mining Society being responsible for £1,263. The Charter, which was granted in 1915, enabled the Institution to standardise the qualifications of mining engineers, and membership of the Institution became a recognition of professional qualifications and experience.

Before the granting of the Charter, members of the federated societies generally used the abbreviation of M.Inst.M.E. (Member of the Institute of Mining Engineers), but there was nothing to stop anyone, however unqualified, from using the letters. The Royal Charter put an end to this abuse. Sir Thomas Holland had said in his presidential address to the Society in 1913, that ease of election to the federated societies had been misused, more often by engineers working abroad.

In 1916 the Institution introduced new rules to strengthen the procedures for the admission of candidates, and new members elected by the individual societies, or whose names had not been added to the federated register, would now also have to be elected by the Council of the Institution. The new rules were formally adopted by the MGMS in February, 1917.

In 1919 rules were further amended with the non-federated status being abolished and strict qualifications of membership enforced. "Members" had to be not less than 30 years old, hold a First Class Certificate of Competency, and have a position of manager, assistant manager, under-manager or chief surveyor. "Associate Members" had to be not less than 23 years old and either be a member of an engineering discipline other than mining or "be a person likely to further the objects of the Society." "Associates" had to be not less than 21 years old and work in mining or an associated industry. Non-federated members of the MGMS were offered the opportunity of transferring to federated status.

Research Committee

By 1917 the geological survey of the Lancashire Coalfield was 50 years old and there was little prospect of a new survey within the next ten or twenty years. The MGMS, which had a particular interest in the survey, together with the University of Manchester and the Lancashire Coalowners Association founded the Lancashire Coal Research Committee. Professor George Hickling, of Manchester University, spent some years on a detailed investigation of the coalfield and his work was published in 1922. Professor Hickling gave papers to the Society, including a summary of the geology of Manchester based on evidence from almost 100 boreholes.

Attempts continued to try and interest mining companies in the Society's activities, and in December, 1916, Lancashire coal companies were sent a circular asking them to subscribe. Initially there were five replies, which brought in an additional income of ten guineas a year.

In 1920 the Society was given notice to quit its premises in John Dalton Street because the owner wanted to put the building up for sale. The building's tenants formed a company to buy the premises, which were then leased back to the original tenants. It cost the MGMS £1,000 to join the company, for which they had to sell some investments, and they took out a 21-year lease on their rooms at a cost of £100 a year.

The year 1920 ended with a curiosity when William Thomas

wrote to the Society in November about a live frog found in a coal seam. The frog appears to have been found by a Mr. Job Lore who sent it to the Society for examination. A letter of thanks was sent to Lore when the frog was returned.

The Hard Years

During the war years, the MGMS had been warned by the writers of various papers of the dire consequences the industry faced unless modern technical education was introduced. Better training would increase the efficiency of the industry and make it better fitted it for competition from Europe and the United States. What could not have been foreseen were the economic conditions which were to rapidly lead to a world-wide recession. Mining engineers were not to escape the bleak economic wind and from the mid-Twenties onwards the Minutes of the MGMS record a growing number of resignations and members falling behind with subscriptions. In 1928 the Society set up a sub-committee to investigate the problem of declining membership, and in 1932 the secretaries of all the federated institutes met in Harrogate to discuss falling rolls. No solutions were found and it was not until after the Second World War that the problem eased.

Trading difficulties apart, the Society continued to play its role within the Lancashire coal trade and took part in various research activities. In May, 1927, the British Colliery Owners' Research Association invited the Society to name some areas of mining which would benefit from research. Professor O.T. Jones suggested an investigation into mining subsidence in the Lancashire Coalfield and this was submitted for consideration. Also established was the Lancashire and Cheshire Safety Mines Research Committee, which included members of the Society and the Lancashire and Cheshire Coal Association. In 1929 the Society had links with the Lancashire Branch of the National Association of Colliery Managers, with whom they discussed a paper from the Mines Research Board.

Manchester Geological Association

Twenty years after federation with the Institution, a move started within the Society for the founding of a Geological Section. In January, 1924, Professor Jones asked Council if more could not be done to further the interests of geology within the Society, and on the suggestion of Sir William Boyd Dawkins, a sub-committee was set up to investigate the proposals. Approval for the new section was given in

March, 1924, and by the following July, 37 members had applied to join. The sub-committee continued its deliberations and in November it had been suggested that a Geological Association, completely separate from the Society, would "better advance the object in view." This the Society agreed to and the Manchester Geological Association, which still thrives today, was given permission to use the MGMS rooms for a token fee of £1 a year.

The Society's library continued to flourish with many new volumes being both bought and presented. In April, 1923, the trustees of Joseph Dickinson's estate offered his library to the Society. Not all the books of the former Inspector of Mines were required and some were offered to the Wigan and District Mining College. Some of Dickinson's annotated volumes are now in the Salford Museum of Mining.

In 1931 extensive plans were made for the Institution summer visit to Manchester, an occasion which was to be fraught with problems. The Lord Mayor told the Society it would not be possible to hold a reception at the Town Hall, and neither would the Institution be able to use the Lord Mayor's parlour for a meeting. Another rebuff came from the University of Manchester, and eventually it was decided to ask the Lord Mayor to greet the visiting engineers at a reception at the College of Technology. Various visits were arranged, including the Mersey Tunnel, Cronton Colliery, the Manchester Ship Canal, Barton Power Station, Metropolitan-Vickers in Trafford Park, Rylands Library and Chethams Hospital. After months of planning came the final blow. Just six days before the visit the Institution asked for the meetings to be postponed "on account of the difficulties...at that time being experienced in the coal industry." A revised date in September was arranged.

Relations with the Institution were not always easy and in December, 1928, a committee was set up to review the history of the Society from the date of federation and "to consider certain difficulties which have arisen from time to time in connection with the qualifications required for membership and with the acceptance of Papers for publication."

The status and qualifications of engineers occupied the attention of the Institution and the Society for many years, and in March, 1934, a report proposed that a voluntary non-statutory Coalmining Engineering Certificate be introduced. Two years later in June, 1936, a committee further recommended that an examination should be set by the I.Min.E., with the cooperation of the Mining Association of Great Britain, and which would, in the first case, be voluntary. In May, 1939, an I.Min.E. committee inquiring into membership reported that in order to raise the status of the Institution, only mining engineers should be admitted as Members or Associate Members. Eminent men could be elected as Honorary Members, said the committee, but other applications would only qualify for Associate status.

A major event in the 1930s was the Society's Centenary. A committee was set up to supervise the celebrations and the Institution was invited to hold its summer meeting in Manchester. E. C. Maitland offered to present a paper on Mining in Lancashire 1838-1938, but unfortunately the paper was not published and only three typed copies were produced by the Society. The Earl of Crawford and Balcarres, whose family had long associations with mining, was elected President for the centenary year.

Outbreak of War

The first hint of the approaching Second World War came in March, 1939, when the Council asked for a paper to be read on Air Raid Precautions at Collieries. A few weeks after the outbreak of hostilities the Society appointed an Emergency Committee with the authority to transfer business and generally deal with all affairs for the duration of the war. Just before Christmas, 1940, Manchester was subjected to extensive bombing raids, and on December 23, Queen's Building was hit by incendiaries. The Society's rooms escaped major damage, but within a few days the Emergency Commitee met and decided to immediately move the library to the Mines Rescue Station at Boothstown, a few miles from the city centre. This decision was to be the beginning of the end for the Society's extensive collection of books, gathered over the past 102 years. Nor was the Society to stay very much longer in the John Dalton Street premises to which they had first moved in 1895. By 1943 the Society decided the premises left much to be desired, and a search began for new rooms.

Initial inquiries came to nothing but in July, 1945, the Society's lease ran out on the Queen's Building, and by the autumn of that year the Society moved to Harvester House in Peter Street, Manchester, for a short-lived tenancy in rooms belonging to Lancashire Associated Collieries. Within a year the Society asked to end the lease, and while rooms for a "nominal headquarters" were sought, meetings were held at the Manchester Engineers Club. Within a few months the Manchester Geological and Mining Society ended its links with the city and moved to accommodation at Wigan and District Mining and Technical College. The Society's library also moved to Wigan where it became part of the college library and looked after by college staff. The library was to survive as an entity until 1965 when the collection was broken up with volumes going to the Institution library, Lancaster University, the National Coal Board archives and Wigan College.

Demand for Engineers

The Society's move to Wigan coincided with vastly improved fortunes for the British coal industry following its nationalisation on January 1, 1947. This major event, of which there is no mention whatever in the Society's Minutes, together with the introduction of the Associate Membership examination by the Institution, were to lead to an influx of new members. The MGMS annual report for 1947 reveals that 32 new members were elected with only eight members resigning, the best figures for many years. Compared with a total membership of 245 in 1939, the membership roll now stood at 311, and by the following year had increased to 318. Britain's desperate post-war need for fuel had lead to rapid mechanisation of the collieries and a resulting demand for qualified engineers.

In May, 1950, the Institution decreed that candidates for Associate Membership should not only hold at least a Second Class Certificate of Competency but should also have have held the position of under-manager for at least a year. MGMS objected to the second qualification, arguing that there were other equally responsible posts in mining. From 1952, admission by election was stopped and only those engineers who had passed the Institution examination could be admitted.

The qualifications for membership of the I.Min.E. continued to be the subject of modification, and in January 1959, MGMS challenged the Memorandum of Guidance for the Members' Election Committee, which recommended a "minimum output requirement" for the collieries in which prospective members worked. This limitation, said the MGMS, could be severe under the then prevailing conditions in the industry, and suggested that managers of collieries which employed more than 30 men underground should also be eligible for membership. In 1963 the MGMS also supported a move to admit to full membership of the I.Min.E. Group Surveyors or surveyors at collieries producing 500,000 tons a year. Until then - as still in 1987 - surveyors who had gained corporate membership of the Royal Institution of Chartered Surveyors were limited to Associate Membership unless they also held a First Class Certificate of Competency, or had passed certain I.Min.E. examinations.

In May, 1964, it was reported that the changing pattern of organisation in the coal industry had lead to a reduction in the number of collieries and an increase in the average size of the surviving mines.

Mining engineers were being appointed to new kinds of positions, such as deputy managers at large mines or specialists with responsibility for reconstruction work or improvements in techniques. Most of the new posts were not in the Qualifications Booklet but the Members' Election Committee agreed that many of these new jobs carried at least the status which had been accepted as a basis for comparison - the equivalent or superior of the manager of a 100,000-ton a year colliery - and agreed to accept them as a qualification for membership.

In 1965 the Council of Engineering Institutions received its Royal Charter and many mining engineers became Chartered Engineers through a service qualification.

To take into account the changing face of the industry and the differing areas of responsibility, new grades of membership were introduced in December, 1969: Members became Fellows (Fellow of the Institution of Mining Engineers); Associate Members became Members (M.I.Min.E.); Honorary Members became Honorary Fellows (Hon.F.I.Min.E.); and the non-corporate grades of Associates and Student Members were unchanged. A new class of non-corporate members was introduced called Associate Members, which covered men not less than 25 years old who were engaged in mining engineering or an ancillary branch or science and who were in the process of qualifying for election as corporate members. In 1987 the categories of membership were: Honorary Fellows; Fellows; Members; Associate Member, for those registered with the Engineering Council as technician engineers; Associate Technician, for those registered as technicians; Students, Associates and Retired Members

Fusion with the NACM

By the early 1960s the industry was faltering after the post-war boom and colliery closures in Lancashire had become common. The declining fortunes of coal also affected the I.Min.E., who, in forecasting a deficit for 1961 of £1,200, called on the federated institutes to encourage recruitment. The MGMS Minutes record a view that fewer young people were entering the industry while other qualified men were leaving to join firms with no mining connections, and "these facts are likely to result in an acute shortage of members."

A major proposal was suggested at the MGMS meeting in November, 1961, by G. Nicholls who felt that two professional bodies - the I.Min.E. and the National Association of Colliery Managers - was wrong, and that a link between the two would be beneficial. Members felt that some change within the Institution was inevitable and that confederation with the NACM was worth further discussion. One matter which did limit membership of the Institution was its requirement that men with a First Class Certificate of Competency who had not taken the I.Min.E examination, could only be classed as Associates, which barred them from voting or holding office.

Manchester led the way in a desire to see changes made in the Institution's constitution, and in 1962 a sub-committee of the Committee of Presidents of the various institutes produced a report on the matter. The President of MGMS, E.J. Kimmins, reported that an amalgamation between the various associations of mining engineers was necessary, but unless pressure was applied the Institution would not agree to such a step. The ideal position would be to have a common body - "say a Royal Society of Mining Engineers" - which could speak for its various branches.

There was great enthusiasm within MGMS for re-constituting the Institution and possible amalgamation with the NACM, and in the following months it was a dominating topic on the agendas. In March, 1963, Kimmins again reported considerable progress at a meeting of the Presidents' Committee, and said that five institutes were in favour of change. After a period when little headway appeared to be made, it was announced that following the setting up of a Joint Committee of the National Association of Colliery Managers and the I.Min.E., that the Institution would, for a limited period, waive the Associate Membership examination and admit to Corporate membership anyone who held a First Class Certificate of Competency. Because this concession was being made for NACM members, it would also apply to I.Min.E Associates and Students over 23 years of age. At this time the Institution had a membership of 4,186 and the NACM a membership of 3,240. Out of the NACM membership 1,767 were also members of the Institution.

Although at national level a merging of the Institution and NACM would not be final until 1969, the secretaries of the MGMS and the North Wales and Lancashire branches of the NACM met in May, 1967, to arrange a joint programme for 1967-68, and by September, 1967, a more complete local "fusion" with the NACM was being discussed. The Institution had suggested that where the territory of an existing federated institute and branch of the NACM was common, that steps be taken to ensure the closest co-operation, by co-opting members of the Council of one body to another and by holding joint meetings and social events. Another meeting of local secretaries was held in October, 1967, where it was agreed that each of the affected branches of the NACM should send two representatives to Council meetings of the MGMS; that all meetings for the following season should be held jointly; and that each President should take the chair at alternate meetings. A final plan for the setting up of a provisional Joint Council of the Lancashire, North Wales and Cumberland branches of the NACM and the MGMS, was approved at a meeting of the Society in October 1968, so that it could be established before the fusion of the two parent bodies.

Fusion of the Institution and the NACM brought major changes and was, technically at least, to bring about the dissolution of the organisation which had been founded as the Manchester Geological Society. In 1971 the Privy Council approved new bye-laws which included a provision that the federated institutes would become branches of the Institution with the result that the direct successor of the MGMS would be known as "The Institution of Mining Engineers - The Manchester Geological and Mining Society Branch". The changes also had important financial implications and the MGMS Branch decided to transfer its investments to the Institution headquarters. By August, 1972, it was reported that dissolution of the old MGMS was complete and that £9,175 would be transferred to the Institution.

Junior Section

In December 1954, a Junior Section of the MGMS was established, initially for engineers under the age of 30, but later the age limit was raised to 35. The Section has made a major contribution to the status of the MGMS as well as providing a forum for the presentation and discussion of technical papers by younger engineers. Past chairmen of the MGMS Junior Section include Sir Robert Haslam, Chairman of the British Coal Corporation, and the 1987-88 President-elect of the Institution of Mining Engineers and a former President of the MGMS Branch, Ken Moses.

In its first few months, the Section visited Golborne Colliery near Leigh, Point of Ayr Colliery, North Wales, and Chisnall Hall Colliery, near Wigan. Similar visits still form an essential part of the annual programme, while the Annual Prize Paper Competition adds a competitive element to the maintenance of standards. One of the highlights of the Section calendar in recent years has been the Annual Symposium where new developments in the field of mining engineering are aired. Attendances of well over 100 are common.

In 1987 there were 80 members of the Branch Junior Section, almost one third of the total membership of MGMS, and recruitment remains an important activity. The Section is also one of eight branches which make up the Institution of Mining Engineers Junior Section at national level, and members of the MGMS branch play an active role. The Chairman and Secretary of the Junior Section also sit on the MGMS Council.

The Future

In 1987, with only 46 members working in the coalfield, the major debating point within the MGMS Branch was its prospects for the future. A working committee was set up to investigate and a questionaire seeking opinions was circulated to the membership. In December, 1986, G. W. Mapp, the President, observed that low attendances at general meetings had been a feature of the Society from its earliest days. With the current state of the coal industry and the closing of collieries throughout Britain, the MGMS Branch was not alone with these problems and the Institution, after discussing the situation on a national basis, had suggested that smaller branches should not merge but should continue to function as independent units; joint meetings with other institutions should be encouraged; that branch council representatives should attend committee and council meetings at national level; and that a minimum of five representatives from each Branch should serve on the Council, which would allow for the development of individuals within Institution affairs.

To stimulate interest at a local level the MGMS Branch decided to hold meetings in the evening; reduce the number of meetings each year to four; introduce a social aspect to meetings which would include either a dinner or buffet and, for the 150th session, to seek speakers of "high standing" who would have the additional qualification of being Lancastrians.

Whether or not the Branch, which began its life in 1838 as the Manchester Geological Society, has run its course, remains to be seen. But in the future, as in the past, its fortunes are tightly bound to the Lancashire Coalfield and its finite reserves.

Dynasties

A number of families active in mining in Lancashire and Cheshire, including the Pilkingtons, Knowles and Greenwells, played roles in the Manchester Geological Society over many years, but the family with the longest connections are the Fletchers, whose association with the industry goes back to the 17th Century.

No records appear to have survived on when the first Fletcher joined the Society, but it must have been at the inaugural meeting or very soon afterwards, for the first mention of John Fletcher, of Bolton, ·is when he resigned in May, 1839. John Fletcher of Clifton is recorded as joining the Society in March, 1858, and this is probably the same person because John Fletcher, who lived at The Hollins, Bolton, was in the 1850s running the Clifton and Kearsley Collieries on behalf of his cousin, as well as being involved in his own flourishing enterprises at

Ladyshore, Little Lever, and Atherton. Also mentioned in the MGS records for 1841 is the membership of a Samuel Fletcher.

John Fletcher's son, Herbert, was also a member of the Society as were Herbert's relatives who ran Atherton Collieries. The Atherton branch of the Fletcher family was always well represented on the membership rolls and included two Ralph Fletchers (father and son), Philip Fletcher, Leonard Fletcher (President in 1914-16), Clement Fletcher (President in 1923-24), and Clement's son, James Fletcher, (President 1958-60).

In 1951 the Society recorded another unusual family achievement when congratulations were sent to Mr W.H. Richards, who together with his three sons, all held First Class Certificates of Competency.

CHAPTER SIX

Coalmining and the Engineers

By 1860 the membership of the Manchester Geological Society had changed its profile from an enthusiastic and knowledgeable band of amateur geologists, to one becoming increasingly dominated by mining engineers. Positive efforts had been made to recruit coal proprietors and engineers, and in the absence of a school of mining, the Society provided a valuable forum for the exchange of opinions, experiences and mining techniques.

In the vanguard of the new breed of member was Joseph Dickinson, one of the first Inspectors of Mines, and an engineer with a vast practical knowledge of the geology of the Lancashire Coalfield. He was elected to the membership in July, 1856.

In contrast was William Boyd Dawkins, whose introduction to the science had come from study at Oxford and duty with the Geological Survey. Dickinson and Boyd Dawkins played important roles in the history of the Geological Society, the first using geological and engineering knowledge to assist in the exploitation of the coal measures, and the other using theoretical ability to establish the existence of the Kent Coalfield and many other important projects.

These two men, outstanding in their respective fields, were amongst many members who were to enhance the status of the Society and take it into the Twentieth Century.

Joseph Dickinson (1818 - 1912)

"He war a gradely guid 'un."

Joseph Dickinson's long and energetic life began in Newcastle-upon-Tyne in November, 1818, and spanned the years of the rapid rise of the British coal industry, in which he was to earn an enviable reputation as mining engineer, practical geologist and Inspector of Mines. He was actively associated with Manchester Geological Society from 1856 until a short time before his death in April, 1912, just a year before coal output in Britain reached a never-to-be-repeated record tonnage.

Dickinson gave many papers to the Society over the years,

principally on mining subjects, but occasionally on subjects as diverse as the Discovery of Rock Salt at Preesal and a eulogy on Sam Short, a winder at St. George's Colliery, Tyldesley, near Manchester, whose dying words, after collapsing at work, showed concern only for the men in his charge.

For seven years the young Dickinson studied in Tyneside under Thomas Sopwith, mining and civil engineer, before moving in 1840 to

Joseph Dickinson

South Wales where he worked for the Dowlais mining and iron company. Dickinson excelled in various aspects of engineering and laid out the first sidings at Cardiff docks. In 1847 he went to the Nithsdale ironworks before starting, in 1850, the most significant part of his career as one of the first four Inspectors of Mines. The vast area in his charge for the first two years covered all of Lancashire, Cheshire, North Wales, Staffordshire, Shropshire and Worcestershire. Later his district was North and East Lancashire, which in 1856 had 240 working collieries.

Dickinson was quickly recognised by both miners and employers as a man of considerable integrity. He showed sympathetic understanding of the conditions under which miners both worked and lived, but was equally sharp in his criticism of men who endangered themselves or their workmates. A miner from Atherton, near Manchester, is said to have paid Dickinson the tribute "He war a gradely guid 'un."

In 1854 the coal trade was doing well and Dickinson observed an increase in the number of fatal accidents. "As usual at such times arising from the hurry to get out quantity, and the greater number of persons employed, as well as perhaps from the irregularities which some of the workpeople are apt to commit in good times, accidents have been numerous," he wrote in his half-yearly report.

Neither were employers safe from censure and prosecution for breaches of the Mining Regulations. Dickinson analysed the cause of increased accidents in his area over the years 1853 - 1854. "...It appears that the increase is mainly in those accidents which are most within the manager's control; whilst those by falls of roof, which in this district depend almost entirely upon the workman, show a diminution; and it is under this head only that there is any diminution."

"The assumption, therefore, seems fair that, on an average, the men are becoming more careful than the masters. Honourable exceptions certainly exist, and the names of some large owners seldom appear in the Black List of Casualties; whilst others, on the contrary, may be found on almost every page, and whom, it seems, it is impossible to stir into vigour without stronger measures than merely inquiring into and pointing out defects," the report continued.

Dickinson was critical of verdicts returned by the courts when poor management was prosecuted, and the lack of compensation for widows and children. "A verdict of manslaughter so seldom occurs that it scarcely operates as a check. Indeed from the result of such verdicts, manslaughter does not appear to apply to colliery accidents," wrote Dickinson. Because of doubt about the law, and the expense of bringing claims, civil proceedings for damages caused by negligence had not been tried "and little or no compensation has been given by the employers to the widow and orphans of the sufferers, except providing a coffin for the deceased," the Inspector went on.

Under Scottish law at that time widows could receive as much as £100, together with £100 for each child. With the support of his superiors, Dickinson had started a case for compensation for the widow of a man killed in an explosion at Moss Hall Colliery, Wigan. At the time of his report in January, 1855, the company had not replied to the claim, and Dickinson thought the case would have to be heard in court. The lawyer engaged to fight the widow's claim was none other than Edward William Binney, of the Manchester Geological Society. Binney took counsel's opinion which stated that on the evidence presented, the widow a had a good prima facie case of action.

Shortly after collaborating with Binney on that case, Dickinson had joined the MGS, probably at the lawyer's instigation. Together with a small number of other members they were to bring fresh life and attract substantial numbers of new members from the field of coal mining.

Dickinson visited collieries in Europe with a colleague in 1853, a journey which led to General Rules on mining safety being introduced through Parliament in 1855. It also gave Dickinson the opportunity to unfavourably compare accident rates in Belgian mines with those in Lancashire pits, where much needed to be done to improve safety consciousness.

After his retirement in 1892 his associates at the Manchester Geological Society, of which he was President four times, subscribe a silver service and an illuminated address. Many were the generous tributes paid to him at the presentation. "He was a born leader of men and his first thought was ever the safety of workmen", said a Mr. Woodward; James Tonge referred to "a means of rescue" Dickinson had devised for pit disasters, and George Wild recited 10 verses which included the lines "The foremost rank he often took in many a noble band," but "His pointedness was forcible in sifting out a flaw."

The Society limited the subscription to Dickinson's testimonial to one guinea per member and raised £85 11s 6d. Presented with the silver- plated tea and coffee service in the Queen Anne style, was a £15 illuminated address, which read:

"Dear Sir, The members of the Manchester Geological Society, with whom you have been associated for so many years as one of the most active and honoured workers, deeply conscious of the many and valuable services you have rendered to the Society both in its geological and mining departments, take the occasion of your retirement from the office of H.M. Senior Chief Inspector of Mines, and after 41 years service, to ask your acceptance of the Address, with the accompanying Service of Silver Plate as a token of their high appreciation of your labours and as a mark of sincere esteem for your conscientious and faithful discharge of duties both in public and private life.

While your past connection with the Society has been an honoured and a helpful one, and, it is to be hoped, not without many pleasant personal memories, your fellow-members still look forward to have your active co-operation in carrying out the objects of the Society for many years to come. In your well-earned release from official duties they trust that you and Mrs. Dickinson will enjoy many years of health and happiness; and that your children, when they look upon this Testimonial, will be stimulated to follow in the father's footsteps, and to be guided by the same high principles which have distinguished his path through life."

Judging from a lecture on Modern and Scriptural Geology which caused a stir at an MGS meeting in 1864, Dickinson appears to have had deep religious convictions which were at that time being severely tested by great advances in geology and other sciences. This topic, in which Dickinson shared in the Victorian Crisis of Belief, is covered more extensively in a later chapter.

By 1908, four years before his death, Dickinson was acclaimed as the Father of the Society, and together with Binney, one of the two outstanding figures in the Society's history. "His work on the coal strata of Lancashire is still the most reliable source of information as to the positions and principle features of the coalfield," says a note in a Society publication. It was also in 1908 that Dickinson, in his 90th year, was made an Honorary Member and also gave probably his last paper to the Society, a brief talk on "The Deviation of Bore-holes."

He remained an active member of the MGS Council for another four years and his last attendance is recorded in the Minutes on April 9, 1912, just 18 days before he died.

Professor Sir William Boyd Dawkins (1837-1929)

In January, 1929, the Manchester Evening News carried an obituary on Professor Sir William Boyd Dawkins, a scientist unrivalled as the outstanding academically active member of the Manchester Geological Society. By chance the newspaper carried on the same page a report of a descent into the workings of the abandoned Channel Tunnel of 1885, a project in which Boyd Dawkins had carried out geological surveys of the French and English coasts. Although the tunnel was quite quickly abandoned, the work Boyd Dawkins had done in the area was to prove invaluable in his research a few years later which led to the proving of the Kent Coalfield.

By repute, Boyd Dawkins had shown precocious interest in geology when only five years old after finding fossils in the coal store at his home in Welshpool. A few years later at Rossall School, Fleetwood, he made a collection of fossils found in the Fylde boulder clay. Boyd Dawkins left Jesus College, Oxford, with a Second in Classics and a First in Natural Science, and joined the Geological Survey for seven years. In 1869 he was elected a member of the Geological Society just as a decision was being reached on the merging of the Society's museum with that of the Manchester Natural History Society at Owens

College. The transfer of the museums was a subject in which Boyd Dawkins was closely interested, for also in 1869 he had been appointed Curator of the Manchester Museum and he was to spend many years organising the collections.

A year later, Boyd Dawkins became lecturer in geology and later the first professor of Geology at Owens College. Eager to further the science of geology, he organised free lectures at the museum and

Professor W. Boyd Dawkins

travelled widely in Lancashire, Cheshire and Yorkshire, lecturing at Mechanics Institutes. In 1882 Boyd Dawkins joined the Scientific Commission on the Channel Tunnel, and a year later laid down a line for another tunnel, destined never to be built, under the Humber.

The project to prove coal under the Cretaceous rocks of Kent began in 1886 when Boyd Dawkins was asked by the directors of the South Eastern Railway to report on the advisability of making a bore hole. If coal did exist it would have improved the fortunes of the railway company and "cause an economic revolution in south-eastern England, as great as that which has been brought about by the working of coal under the chalk in France and Belgium."

Boyd Dawkins gave two papers to the Geological Society on the search for the Kent coal, and in February, 1897, he delivered a stinging rebuke to the authors of another paper on the new coalfield which had been read at a meeting of the Federated Institution of Mining Engineers at Wigan. The paper, by Brady, Simpson and Griffiths, credited Brady, Engineer to the South Eastern Railway, with the idea of sinking the borehole which proved the coal measures, and made no mention of Boyd Dawkins. "As one of the prime movers it becomes my duty to record the facts ....while all those who are concerned in the matter are alive, and while all the documentary evidence is to hand."

Boyd Dawkins told the MGS meeting in February, 1897. "The importance of the discovery raises the matter above the level of an ordinary difference of opinion, and its probable far-reaching results...lend a value to personal details otherwise dull and unprofitable. It is ...a matter not of opinion, but of fact," said Boyd Dawkins before giving the Society a brief history of the theory and practice which led to the establishment of the Kent coal industry. Boyd Dawkins acknowledged that as long ago as 1826 the coalfield of Somerset had been said to have a physical identity with that of northern France. In 1855 Godwin Austen wrote a paper on the possible extension of the coal measures beneath south-east England and following the Coal Commission of 1866-71, one of the Commissioners had concluded that the Somerset Coalfield and those of Northern France and Belgium "were represented in south-eastern England by long narrow east and west troughs, concealed beneath the lower rocks."

In 1871 Boyd Dawkins and Henry Willett put down a borehole at Netherfield, near Battle, which ended in Oxford Clay and proved that the oolites were more than 1,700 feet thick. From this trial Boyd Dawkins declared that it was obvious that the North Downs offered the best position for a fresh attempt, where both oolites and Wealden strata thinned off against "the axis of the artois." Boyd Dawkins, Willett and a Mr. Whittaker had considerable faith in such a new site that they planned in 1884-85 to put down an experimental borehole. In the spring of 1886 the railway company stepped in and asked Boyd Dawkins for help in proving the coal measures. The site chosen for the borehole was at the Channel Tunnel works at Shakespeare Cliff, Dover, "to prove the westward extension of the Calais measure, which...are only 27 miles to the east."

Boyd Dawkins forecast that the older rocks would be met at 1,000 feet or less, and he was retained by the railway company to carry out the geological supervision of the project. Brady, the railway company engineer, together with a Mr Pigou, had the responsibility for carrying out the boring. Before the discovery of the coalfield in 1890, Boyd Dawkins' responsibility was the examination of the cores and identifying fossils and rock. With the coal measures proved, it then only remained to determine the commercial value of the discovery, and the problems of mining, in which a further six experts were consulted. On July 1, 1891, Boyd Dawkins, C. Tylden Wright, and Fras. Brady, reported to the railway company directors: "Having carefully considered the general samples of coal that have been obtained, we are of the opinion that the evidence in favour of workable coal is sufficient to justify a trial shaft being put down immediately on the site of or near to the present boring."

The Manchester Geological Society was told that Boyd Dawkins was responsible for the geological part of the enterprise; Sir Edward Watkin, Chairman of the railway company had the credit for translating geological theory into fact, and that Brady had nothing to do with the geology whatever. Boyd Dawkins did admit though that in 1882 Brady had suggested to Sir Edward Watkin that "the coal question could be tested ...with the men retained under him to maintan the Channel Tunnel works." That idea though had not been acted upon and "the claim may safely be left without further comment to the judgment of those who are interested in discovery," he added.

The Kent Coalfield was just one of many projects on which Boyd Dawkins worked and in the last two decades of the 19th Century his talents were in demand throughout the world. An authority on water supplies, he advised on schemes for several major towns and cities, including London and Liverpool, and reported on projects as diverse as the Manchester Ship Canal and oil shales in New South Wales. He was President of the Geological Society from 1874-77 and again from 1886-87. Amongst papers he read to the Society were The Antiquity of Man, Climate During the Pleistocene Age, Geography of Britain in the Carboniferous Age, Carboniferous Flora, and observations on the finding of a mammoth at Northwich, Cheshire.

Boyd Dawkins, a committed Liberal, also showed social concern and made an attempt to gain compensation for people affected by subsidence caused by brine pumping in the Northwich area of Cheshire. Although his campaign was unsuccessful, facts he had gathered were later used to push helpful legislation through Parliament. He was professor of geology at Owens and Manchester University for 34 years. In his later life he was awarded honours, both academic and public, and was knighted in 1919.

CHAPTER SEVEN

The Transactions

The Transactions of the Manchester Geological and Mining Society, even though not totally complete, are a valuable record of the expansion of geological knowledge and the advance of mining techniques and expertise over a century and a half. Early active members of MGS such as Bowman, Binney, and G.W. Ormerod, helped to lay the foundations of a modern science and were generally aware of the limitations of knowledge of the age they lived in. In a paper on the "Geology of Manchester and its Vicinity" in 1839, Binney wrote: "Some of the information furnished to the author, as well as his own observations, may possibly be incorrect; none, however, will rejoice more than himself in seeing any misconceptions or errors, into which he may have fallen, rectified."

Professor Williamson wrote to the Society in 1886 saying: "My past researches have been chiefly remarkable for the revelation they have made to me of the vast measure of my own ignorance; It is almost humiliating.

"Nevertheless I am still obtaining glimpses of the figure of Truth gliding in the distance, though in a somewhat hazy form; and I am not without hope that I shall yet add a few more photographs of Her, to those which I have already obtained," he added in the letter thanking the Society for making him an honorary member.

Professor Williamson was another outstanding scientist who adopted Manchester as his home. Born in Scarborough, he was acquainted with William Smith, the father of British geology, a friend of John Dalton and prominent member of Manchester Literary and Philosophical Society. He preceded Thomas Brown as curator of the museum of the Manchester Natural History Society and was associated with both Huxley and Darwin. The building which now houses the Geological Department of the University of Manchester is named after him.

The contents of papers read to the Society were also influenced by wider outside events. The paper which Bowman read to the Society in 1840 on The Origin of Coal, is a distillation of available knowledge, some postulation of what he hoped would be proved, and religious influence. It is, in fact, a paper of its time.

Almost 25 years later there was considerable agitation amongst some members of the Society over a paper on "Modern and Scriptural Geology" read by Joseph Dickinson. This paper showed the concern that the rapid advance of science was having on religious belief, and in Dickinson's case showed great personal turmoil in coming to terms with geological research and discovery.

A hint of what was to come ocurred at a meeting on December 22, 1863, when Edward Hull read a paper on glacial striations at Bidston Hill, near Birkenhead. Dickinson told Hull: "I think you are jumping to a conclusion in attributing them (striations) to icebergs. It is not unusual in the roof of coal seams to see these groovings, which are occasioned by rocks sliding over each other." As he intended to present a paper on the subject he would not expand further on his thoughts. Hull asked his audience not to be led astray by Dickinson's assertations because "there is nothing more certain than the grooving of rock surfaces is the result of ice." Hull was supported by Binney who said Dickinson was going rather far back in geology and not looking at it as it was considered at the present day. "There are some things laid down distinctly and authoritively and one of them is that ice has acted very extensively in the drift deposits."

A month later, on January 19, 1864, Dickinson read a paper on "Modern and Scriptural Geology." There is no mention of the lecture in the Minutes of that meeting but it caused such a furore that a week later a special Council meeting was called to discuss it. Present at the special meeting were Andrew Knowles, A.M. Ormerod, W.R. Barr, Thomas Farrimond, G.C. Greenwell, J.J. Horsfall and J.E. Forbes. Dickinson was a notable absentee. There were just two resolutions on the agenda and both were passed without any comment being made in the Minutes:

1. It was resolved that Mr. Dickinson's paper entitled "Modern and Scriptural Geology" be not printed in the Transactions of the Manchester Geological Society.

2. It was resolved that the secretaries be instructed to request Mr. Dickinson to withdraw his paper - "Modern and Scriptural Geology" - for publication in the Transactions of the MGS.

Dickinson's reaction to the special meeting is not indicated but it does appear that he went on to privately publish a revised version of the lecture. It was this publication which led to a vitriolic letter being written, critical of both Dickinson and the MGS, to the Mining Journal on February 27, 1864, by a correspondent who sheltered behind the nom-de-plume Mentor.

By 1864 Dickinson enjoyed an excellent reputation as a mining engineer and in the annual reports of the Inspectorate of Mining he shows great compassion for workers in the industry. From the comments made by Mentor, Dickinson also appears to have been a man of deep and fundamental religious conviction. It was a combination of his belief and his attempts to come to terms with the conclusions of modern geology which led to his strange lecture to the MGS.

Dickinson, it seems, tried to reconcile geology with a literal interpretation of the Bible. "...the Inspector adhered like a limpet to the everlasting rock of orthodoxy, and in this adhesion appears to have lost sight of all and everything pertaining to the very strata from which he derives his sustenance," wrote Mentor. In a summary of the lecture, Mentor says Dickinson claimed, amongst other things, that pumice stone might be the result of spontaneous combustion; that all things were originally in a watery state and that even now rocks were so moist that a current of air driven through them became damp; that if the theory on sedimentary rocks were admitted, deposits would be mixed...and never found in immense beds; and that pebbles did not drift by glaciers but were formed on the spot.

"The distortion of facts and the utter absence of fair logical deductions from those assumed, are too obvious to require remark," Mentor continued. "The paper is discreditable to the society and as well as to its author.....and in saying this much we deal very tenderly with both of them."

In the March 5 edition of the Mining Journal, John Atkinson, Secretary of the Manchester Geological Society, stung by Mentor's remarks about the Society, wrote in reply: "The paper published by Mr. Dickinson is not the paper which that gentleman read at a meeting of the MGS in January, which the Council...refused to print." "The published document being, however, in the main a re-hash of the one which was rejected by our council, it may be right to satisfy the curiosity of your correspondent, and also of your readers, as to how such a paper was allowed to be read.

"...The practice of our society...is to announce for reading any paper, the title of which is sent to the secretaries a reasonable time before the meeting at which it is intended to be brought forward. In general the character of each member is a sufficient guarantee that nothing absurd or derogatory to the reputation of the society will be offered. "Up to the time of the reading of the rejected paper, notwithstanding the contemptuous sneers of "Mentor", neither Mr. Dickinson's well-known ability, his experience as a geologist, nor the character of his papers printed in our society's Transactions, seemed to require the secretaries to apply any other rule to the announcement of a paper by him than that which had always been applied to those of other members.

"Hence it was that the paper was announced....and read in spite of the earnest remonstrances, and deprecatory intercession of some of his friends, who had become aware of its purport," added the MGS Secretary. Atkinson also pointed out that the Manchester Lit and Phil had endured a lecture which sought to prove that solar rays were a compound of oxygen and hydrogen, because in admitting rays into a bottle in a certain way, there was a deposit of moisture on the inside of the glass. The British Association too had heard a paper from a gentleman, "holding an honourable social position," who claimed to show he could extract the square root of the number two in finite terms; and that he had obtained, also in finite terms, the proportion between the diameter and circumference of a circle - "in other words, he had squared the circle!" he added. The MGS, said Atkinson, could not be said to have disgraced itself because a few of its members listened to a "silly paper" which it immediately repudiated.

Atkinson's letter to the Mining Journal did not please the Council of the MGS, and discussion of the matter at a meeting on March 29 was postponed until Atkinson could be present and the letter by Mentor produced. Atkinson immediately resigned as Secretary, to the apparent regret of the Council which called on him, at a meeting on 26 April 1864, to reconsider. The Council felt "quite sure that he wrote the letter to the Mining Journal under the impression that such letter was necessary and the council did not see any reason now to discuss the letter." Tragically Atkinson died before the matter could be finally resolved and at a Council meeting on May 31, 1864 the Council expressed its sorrow at the death "of their late respected Secretary ...and to accord their sense of loss the society has sustained in the removal of our officer who has devoted so much time and attention to its interests."

The Dickinson affair also drew another letter to the columns of the Mining Journal. H. Rhys said Mentor's letter went beyond the verge of fair criticism....and that he had written a personally offensive letter which could not hurt Dickinson nor damage his theory. "It is not more cowardly to hit a man when he is down than it is to abuse a man personally because he ventures to put forward theories of his own in opposition to those generally received. What on earth has Mr. Dickinson's position as Inspector of Collieries to do with the method in which the world was built?" Rhys did not agree with Dickinson's theories but said "the objections which he urges against modern geology are a stumbling block to him in common with some of the more experienced geologists of the day."

Rhys exposed the inadequacies of geological science in the 1860s when he challenged Mentor to explain how the Silurian rocks of Wales

72

which, according to "modern geology were deposited in a horizontal position, were bent and thrown into those wonderful curves." "Did he (Mentor) ever calculate how much larger the area was which they covered when flat to that which they now occupy," wrote Rhys.

Neither were practitioners of geology like Dickinson the only ones to expose themselves to criticism largely as a result of their reluctance to accept theoretical conclusions. In 1892 Dickinson himself drew the attention of the MGS to a letter written by Sir Roderick Murchison, when a member of a Royal Coal Commission, in which the distinguished geologist claimed in 1871 that the existence of any productive coalfields in the South Eastern counties of England was improbable in the highest degree. Only a few years later Professor Boyd Dawkins proved him wrong.

Dickinson did not appear to suffer any lasting damage to his reputation as a result of the 1864 furore and at meetings later that year he played an active part in Society discussions and in the years ahead he was to read many creditable papers and be sought for his professional opinions. Just over 40 years later Dickinson returned to a mystical theme on the origin of life in a brief paper, which on this occasion, was printed in the Transactions.

Soon after the turn of the century a theory had been proposed that radium had played a major role in the origin of life. In November, 1905, Dickinson refuted the radium theory but remarked that "among fossils, man no where seems to appear." "Assuming that fossils once lived, how did the life originate? Life is associated with matter. Matter is convertible but indestructable. How did it begin? The combination, with renewed sustenance, continues for a time, each part influencing the other. If unhastened by ills, it terminates with age. It is an intricate problem to demonstrate," went on the 85-year-old mining engineer. "The most ancient view of the beginning is the Mosaic narration, which is accepted by many as revelation and by some as Egyptian tradition. The order and accompaniments mentioned are: Creation, apparently with fossil life during ages; then stupendous divisions, followed by vegetation, fish, fowl, beast, and man formed from dust breathed into. The further enlightenment has to be searched out. Be it through radium or something else, research such as that which discovered spectrum analysis and the atomic theory, may find this out also," he ended.

Professor W. Boyd Dawkins, for rather more scientific reasons, also disagreed with the radium theory, and held that the solution to the problem of the origin of life was no nearer then than when Professor Huxley had confessed himself baffled by it.

In the field of mining the Society showed a concern for industrial issues which often preceded legislation by some years. Coal dust explosions in mines were discussed many years before the 1912 Coal Mines Act laid down regulations. The question of the safety of miners' lamps was discussed at great length for many Victorian decades, with tests being held, comparisons made and hopes being expressed for the introduction of safe electric lamps. Other national mining issues such as the introduction of new explosives, overwinding devices, and even the strength of timber used for pit props had a generous airing at Society meetings.

Mines Rescue and Garforth

One vital area in which Lancashire mining companies lead the way was in the provision of central mines rescue stations, the first in the country being opened at Howe Bridge, Atherton, in 1908, and followed within a few years by a network of stations in all the coalfields.

W.E. Garforth, of Altofts Colliery, near Normanton, Yorks, President of the MGMS in 1909-1910, had played a leading role in mining safety for many years and had organised the construction of a training gallery at Altofts in 1899 where miners could be instructed in realistic conditions for rescue work. He also designed the Weg breathing apparatus and in March, 1907, gave a demonstration to members of the Society. The first Weg life-saving device had been built at Altofts, and the prototype weighed a sturdy 30lbs, which Garforth was sure could be reduced when made professionally. It contained enough oxygen for two and a half hours for a man under exertion, or six hours at rest. The purifier contained about two and a half pounds of caustic potash and caustic soda which absorbed carbon dioxide given off by the wearer.

Life-saving devices had occupied scientific minds for many generations, and Joseph Dickinson told the same meeting that as early as 1825 "An Apparatus to enable Persons to Breath in Thick Smoke or in Air loaded with Suffocating Vapours" had won a prize of 50 guineas from the Royal Society of Arts. The inventor, John Roberts, had made an apparatus consisting of a mask with goggles and inhaling arrangements through the interstices of a sponge immersed in varied saturated solutions of lime-water, chloride of lime, caustic soda and sometimes pure water, according to the impurity to be met with, said Dickinson. In a colliery fire in 1851, Dickinson had used a breathing device invented five years earlier, which incorporated bags of Glauber salts and lime. Dickinson said the device had been used for some hours, but the explorers were sick and the bags discarded.

Garforth also carried out very important experiments on the

explosive qualities of coal dust, and made the topic the subject of his presidential address in May, 1910. There had been considerable controversy over the dangers of coal dust and it took many long and painful decades for it to become accepted as a major cause of devastating explosions. The effect of coal dust being ignited by an explosion of methane had first been noted by John Buddle in 1803, and in 1845 Michael Faraday had given a talk on the subject to the Royal Institution. Early experimental work had been on too small a scale, said Garforth, and it was not until after the Courrieres disaster in France in 1907 in which 1,100 men died, that Europe's first reasonably-sized experimental gallery had been built. In 1908 experiments began at a gallery at Altofts Colliery.

A Royal Commission on Coal Dust in Mines which sought to settle the controversy had first sat in 1891, but it was only with the setting up of the Royal Commission on Mines in 1906 that practical steps were taken. Garforth was asked to organise the experiments at Altofts to show the explosive nature of coal dust and air without the presence of gas; to find a way of stopping coal dust explosions, and to investigate the chemical and physical phenomena of coal dust explosions. Garforth, who was knighted for his work in 1913, gave a detailed description of the experimental gallery and the effectiveness of stone dust in stifling explosions. The practical effects of the Garforth-led experiments were shown in the 1911 Coal Mines Act which laid down stringent regulations covering coal dust.

Evidence to the 1891 Commission on Coal dust in Mines was given, on behalf of the Manchester Geological Society, by its President, Mr John S. Burrows, of the Fletcher Burrows Company of Atherton, near Manchester. Burrows told the inquiry that although he thought coal dust was an additional danger in mines it was an opinion which might not be shared by all members of MGS.

After an explosion in one of his company's pits at Lovers Lane, Atherton, in 1872, in which 27 men died, he had noticed coked dust on the pit props after the accident, but had only considered coal dust as a factor in explosions after the Seaham disaster in 1880. There was evidence that before the Seaham accident, coal dust at least an inch thick lay on the timber roof supports and a man retreating after firing an overcharged shot had kicked up more dust from the floor. Burrows said he had changed the lighting on the screens at Atherton from gas to electricity after noticing that on windy days the gas jets flared to two or three times their normal size as a result of coal dust in the air. Watering of work places was by no means a complete answer to keeping down dust, and Burrows said that Atherton Collieries chiefly relied on using Carbonite, a flameless explosive. He would, he told the inquiry, ban gunpowder altogether.

Henry Hall, an Inspector of Mines and member of MGS, carried out tests on coal dust explosions in 1893 at White Moss Colliery, Lancashire. In The Mining Engineer, November 1986, Irvin Saxton described the experiments in the 50-yard deep shaft which was ventilated by a hand-driven surface fan through ten-inch iron tubes. Samples of coal dust from 45 different collieries were tested. Individual samples of at least 5cwt were tipped down the shaft before a cannon loaded with one and a half pounds of gunpowder was fired. In almost every case a violent explosion occurred, the exceptions being anthracite and coal dust from the Forest of Dean. Hall recommended that gunpowder should be banned in coalmines in favour of high explosives.

Ventilation: A different View

Efficient ventilation had always been regarded as a necessity for the safe running of a colliery and reducing the chances of explosions. Mining engineers who had had this principle instilled in them for all their working lives, showed some surprise at a special general meeting at Manchester University in February, 1912, when Dr John Harger gave a paper on "The Prevention of Explosions in Mines," which expounded a simple method of preventing dust explosions, firedamp explosions, and fires. The lecture was to arouse considerable interest both within the Society and in the public domain, receiving newspaper coverage and being the subject of a question in the House of Commons. It also brought a strong response from distinguished mining authorities.

Harger, of Liverpool University, had carried out investigations into how much atmospheric oxygen was needed to support various flames. A candle required 16.9 to 17 per cent oxygen before extinguishing; petroleum (burned through a wick) 16.9 per cent; and methane about 17.5 per cent. Harger's contentious theory was that if the oxygen content of ventilation air was reduced from the normal 21 per cent then explosions would not occur. He also produced figures which he claimed showed that of 28 samples of coal dust, none would explode if the oxygen content of the air was at 18 per cent with an additional 1.5 per cent of carbon dioxide.

He dismissed claims that air which would not support the flame of a candle was not fit to breath, and said that an examination of exhaled air showed that only a small amount of oxygen had been used. His tests showed that the respired air, after removal of water vapour, had 3.5 to 4 per cent carbon dioxide, 16.5 to 17 per cent oxygen, and

79.5 per cent nitrogen. "As so little of the total amount of oxygen in the air is used in breathing it may well be asked: Is it necessary to have so much more than we use? The answer is: No, it is not," said the scientist. "No one would know that he was breathing anything different or unusual if a supply of 17.5 per cent of oxygen with 82.5 percent of nitrogen were put into a room to replace the ordinary air," he went on.

Harger, who apparently had no practical mining experience, said that a report of the British Coal Dust Committee in 1910 had remarked: "The impossibility of preventing an explosion taking place by depriving it of oxygen necessary to propagate combustion is so manifest that it need not be enlarged upon." In Harger's opinion this was the simplest means of preventing explosions. Harger's lengthy and complex paper claimed that large dust explosions unaided by gas were a modern phenomena and were caused by the Coal Mines Regulation Act of 1872 which had led to an increase in ventilation currents, "thus removing the many small fire-damp explosions with the right hand, and giving the few big dust explosions with the left."

"The only way to prevent absolutely coal-dust explosions is to leave nothing to chance," said Harger. "A reduction of one per cent in the oxygen content, and the addition of half a per cent of carbon dioxide in the ventilating current, is all that is required for most mines; and for the more dangerous mines - those with inflammable dusts - a reduction of two per cent in the oxygen content and the addition of about three quarters to one per cent of carbon dioxide would make the intake ways absolutely safe. The practice of having doors between the intakes and returns should be avoided as much as possible; only absolutely essential ones should be left, and these made very small and strong. Coal mines could be made absolutely safe from explosions of dust and firedamp, and fires, by reducing the amount of oxygen in the air to 17.5 per cent," said Harger.

Reduction of the oxygen in the atmosphere, said Harger, could be achieved by introducing flue gases into the ventilation system. Care would have to be taken to guard against the formation of carbon monoxide and dust, smoke and sulphur dioxide would have to be removed. Harger dismissed the practical problems by saying that "some simple plant would be necessary but the capital outlay would be small".

Harger's paper found little favour with the practical mining engineers. George B. Harrison, President of the Society, and an Inspector of Mines, said Harger's views ran counter to those which they had held for a lifetime, and whether Harger would be quite as sure of his facts if they were put into practice, remained to be seen. Alfred J. Tonge, of Hulton Collieries, asked if Harger had collected sufficient data to make certain that he had reached a final conclusion. Among the several members who put forward strong practical objections, was George H. Winstanley, who said even if it was possible to overcome the insuperable problems of putting Harger's proposal into operation, the proposal was based on an entirely fallacious assumption, that the excess of oxygen which the normal atmosphere of a mine provided could be dispensed with. Doctor Harger invited those in charge of coalmines to sacrifice, or at least impair, the margin of safety, but a long record of past mining fatalities and mining experience forbade such a thing, said Winstanley, who also challenged Harger to prove that the health of miners would not suffer in working under the conditions proposed. Leonard Fletcher also remarked on the problems miners could face in working in an atmosphere of 17.5% oxygen and then re-adjusting to normal atmosphere at the end of the shift.

Two months after the paper was read, it was again the subject of considerable further detailed discussion and criticism at a Society meeting. Despite Harger's statement that large dust explosions were a modern event and caused by the 1872 Act, Harrison said that but for great improvement in mine ventilation the loss of life by explosion would have been greater still. Ninety-four year-old Joseph Dickinson, making his last contribution to a Society discussion before his death later that month, said Harger's proposal was not in accordance with what had been aimed at since 1850, and it would take some time to persuade miners that improvement was to be effected by sending in impure air.

Sir Henry Hall said the idea of working in an atmosphere into which certain unpleasant gases had been added, and from which a certain amount of oxygen had been removed, did not appeal to him. Scientists and engineers from all over the country, including Professor W.M. Thornton, of Newcastle, Dr. J.S. Haldane, of Oxford, Dr Leonard Hill, of London Hospital and Professor W. Galloway, of Cardiff, wrote to the Society expressing informed criticism on the controversial paper. Despite the doubts cast upon his theory, Harger put up a spirited defence and said that Pretoria Pit at Over Hulton, near Bolton, scene some 18 months earlier of an explosion which killed 344 men and boys, was probably one of the most excessively ventilated collieries in the kingdom, and in the old days only a few men would have been burned near where the ignition took place. Harger's claim was refuted in a later discussion by Harrison who said he had no knowledge of over-ventilated pits, most of which were under-ventilated. Harger returned to the MGMS to give talks on "Gob-fires and the Prevention of Gob-fires in Mines," (October, 1912) and in November, 1913, he gave two papers, "The Detection of Gob fires" and "Firedamp in Coal Mines and the Prevention of Explosions." On each occasion his papers provoked lively discussion.

Love for the Steam Engine

Lancashire mining men could be cautious in introducing new ideas, and were criticised in 1909 when Gerald H.J. Hooghwinkel gave a paper on exhaust-steam turbines. He claimed that Lancashire's pits had made very little headway in the introduction of electrical power for pumping, winding and haulage compared to South Wales, Durham and Yorkshire. The major reason for the reluctance to invest in electric power was probably financial due to some pits only having a short life. "Another argument, mostly brought forward by electrical engineers, is the assumed inherent love for the steam engine as a local product," complained Hooghwinkel.

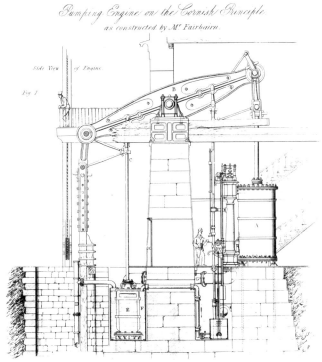

Pumping Engine on the Cornish Principle as constructed by Mr Fairbairn

A more substantial reason supported by colliery engineers was the "excellent efficiency ascribed to such existing systems as rope-driven haulage...also smaller districts underground requiring less haulage away from the pit bottom."

Falls: Major Cause of Death

Explosions provided dramatic evidence of the dangers of coal mining, but George B. Harrison, in his presidential address in 1911, said that falls of roof or sides claimed almost three times as many lives. From 1873 to 1910, explosions had killed 6,305 men and boys, while falls of ground had killed 18,161. Accidents in shafts had claimed 3,605 fatalities, while another 9,595 had died in various other underground accidents.

During 1910, which had seen major disasters at Pretoria Pit, Over Hulton, and at Whitehaven in which 136 men died, there had been a total number of deaths by explosions of 501, compared to 636 from falls of ground and a total loss of life amongst underground workers of 1,622. Harrison blamed the high toll of death from falls of ground to lack of attention to propping the roof and sides. Special rules introduced into mines were in most cases the result of conferences, compromises and final agreement between owners, employees, the local Inspector of Mines, and the Home Office, and were generally short of current advanced practice.

Some 50 years earlier the managers of one colliery had introduced a method of propping which had proved so effective that no accidents from fall of roof had ever been reported, despite an annual output of 100,000 tons for all that time. Stricter management, said Harrison, would help reduce this type of accident, and firemen, who were the officials closest to the job, could play an important role. Managers should personally see that notices giving maximum distances between props or other roof supports could be understood and carried out, and also ensuring that a good supply of props, bars and cappings was provided.

John Gerrard, a retired Inspector of Mines, told the Society in January, 1915, that discipline was an essential feature in mine safety, and any weakness by officials supervising timbering at the coalface was absolutely fatal. Delay in setting supports or props was dangerous, and although timbering distances had then been fixed, the idea had been badly carried out and miners had scarcely regarded the matter.

Many accidents also occurred in withdrawing timber from the waste, and much could be done by adopting safe-distance withdrawing appliances, such as the Silvester pulling jack. He condemned the use of the short hammer in removing props, and said that miners had to get so close to the prop being removed that there was no chance of escape if the roof fell. The use of temporary supports was also very often omitted, and the use of these as a means of saving life should be greatly extended. Further problems in timbering in the Lancashire Coalfield were caused by the heavy dips of the strata.

CHAPTER EIGHT

Pit Disasters and Legislation

In the first decade of the Twentieth Century there was a great deal of public discussion on major legislation affecting the mining industry, and members of the Manchester Geological and Mining Society played their part. Three major pieces of mining legislation, the 1908 Eight Hours Act, the 1911 Coal Mines Act and the 1912 Minimum Wage Act, together with the 1913 Trade Union Act, presented a formidable amount of legislation to be absorbed in a short number of years.

The first years of the new century also brought a great deal of grief to Lancashire mining communities. On August 18, 1908, 75 men were killed in an explosion at the Maypole Colliery, at Abram, and the MGMS expressed its sorrow. John Gerrard, an Inspector of Mines, said they had hoped that such great disasters were a thing of the past and the Society would have to give renewed attention to considering how such events could be prevented. An inquest decided the explosion was caused by firedamp and coal dust being ignited by the firing of a shot, and criticised supervision in the pit during the absence on holiday of the manager.

In November 1910, A. J. Tonge, general manager of Hulton Collieries, near Bolton, was President of the Society. In a grimly prophetic Presidential Address on safety in mining, he said: "I am particularly thinking about those classes of accidents which affect so heavily the annual returns and which every now and then come with a sudden shock upon us because of the number of fatalities at one fell swoop..." Six weeks later on December 21, 1910, 344 men and boys died at Hulton Collieries when an explosion devastated No 3 Bank Pit, or Pretoria as it was commonly known. An inquiry concluded that gas and coal dust had been ignited by a faulty or overheated safety lamp. At its meeting in January, 1911, members of the Manchester Geological and Mining Society stood in silence and a resolution was passed expressing sympathy with the bereaved.

These two Lancashire disasters, together with a third at Whitehaven in 1910 in which 136 men died, were to have great influence in the drafting of safety regulations in the 1911 Coal Mines Act. While the Bill was progressing through the House of Commons its provisions were discussed at great length at MGMS meetings and the Society sent a delegation to the House of Commons to lobby the Home Secretary, Winston Churchill, on various points. Seven members, Alfred J. Tonge, John S. Burrows, Sir Henry Hall, Sydney A. Smith, Scott Barrett, Percy Lee Wood and George H. Hollingworth, travelled to London on May 22, 1911, but Churchill was not available and they made their views known to an under-secretary.

The deficiencies of the 1911 Act were discussed in a paper to the Society in June, 1914, by A. Drury Mitton, who questioned whether the Act should have been more definite in some of its provisions. So far as ventilation went, the new Act had adopted, with only little amendment, a form of words from the 1887 Mines Regulation Act which stated "that an adequate amount of ventilation shall constantly be produced to render harmless all noxious gases, etc." Mitton thought the 1911 Act could have put more responsibility on colliery managers to state in writing to Inspectors of Mines the quantity of air per cubic foot per minute which was neccessary for each man, boy and horse, and have the same quantity produced daily and measured and recorded.

Another important omission, said Mitton, was that the 1911 Act did not provide for the ventilation of roads not in use. Normal custom at collieries was to drive narrow roads for prospecting, and this was being done at the time of the disasters at Pretoria and Whitehaven. Mitton thought that where roads were not in use they should either be kept entirely free from accumulations of gas, or built so that no gas could escape in dangerous quantities. The 1911 Act also allowed the haulage of coal in return airways providing that an Inspector had carried out six tests for gas over a period of twelve weeks and found less than a half per cent of gas in the atmosphere. The danger from having haulage in the return airway came from the number of lamp-carrying men and the possibility of sparks being given off by the friction of ropes on rollers. Mitton pointed out that sudden blowers of gas were common and places were holed into near faults and gas given off, so that a return airway might at any time be totally unfit for haulage. Coal haulage in return air roads was bad mining, said Mitton, and should be banned.

Mitton listed a number of other items which he felt the 1911 Act did not cover adequately, before severely criticising the Act for allowing the unlocking and relighting of lamps at underground lamp stations. "...within a short time of the Act becoming law the explosion at Senghenydd Colliery (South Wales) occurred in which 439 lives were lost," said Mitton. "The conclusions arrived at after the inquiry suggest that the explosion may have originated by a blower of gas issuing from a heavy fall of stone and igniting itself at the underground lamp station."

Mitton said it was well known at the Home Office during the time the Act was being compiled that at some of the best managed and fiery collieries no safety-lamp was ever allowed to be unlocked or relit underground on any pretext whatever. In these mines spare lamps were taken underground every day ready for emergency in case a miner should lose his light. "Why, then, should not this precaution have been brought into vogue long ago...and statutory provision made for carrying into effect what is now stigmatised, after a disaster of this magnitude has occurred, as a dangerous practice, when such facts were clearly known beforehand?" he asked.

Mitton's paper raised a great deal of discussion, and Leonard Fletcher, of Atherton Collieries, said that while he was in favour of most of Mitton's suggestions, he felt the Act did not allow enough discretion to the management. A.J.A. Orchard, of St Helens, said safety depended more on improved knowledge and discipline, and the colliery manager had little appetite for more legislation. Mitton, in reply, said he did not intend to increase legislation but to ask whether certain technical points might not be amplified to secure greater safety.

The onset of the First World War heralded dramatic change for the British coal industry. Within a year of war being declared, some 250,000 experienced miners - one quarter of the workforce - had joined the armed forces with the result that coal output slumped and threatened the war effort. An added strain on the British industry was that coalmines in France and Belgium had fallen into enemy hands.

A Government committee was set up to investigate how coal production could be maintained and a survey of some of the problems facing the industry formed the basis of the 1915 presidential speech to the Society, by Leonard Fletcher. A mild winter and economies by householders would help reduce demand, he said, but increasing output brought a number of problems. Increasing the number of working hours would not necessarily increase production, and Fletcher cited figures for 1910 when coal output in the first full year of the implementation of the Eight Hour Act was actually greater than two years previously. His opinion was that many Government works had lost more than they had gained by introducing seven-day working instead of six.

Despite these misgivings, Fletcher felt the Eight Hour Act was too rigid, and needed amendment in many small details, and an appreciable increase of output could take place if there were more latitude. Absenteeism was another major problem, with the Lancashire and Cheshire coalfield heading the list with an absenteeism rate of 10.4

per cent "after making every allowance for the unavoidably absent." High absenteeism was confined to some 17.5 per cent of the work force, with the vast majority of men having a good record of work.

On November 12, 1918, the day after the hostilities ended, A.J.A. Orchard gave a detailed breakdown to the Society on how the war had affected the St Helens Collieries. By the end of 1915, 895 men had enlisted out of a total workforce of 1,826, and by 1918 this figure had grown to 1,276 or 58 per cent of the pre-war total. The sudden loss of these men, particularly those in skilled trades, had greatly affected the running of the colliery, and several districts had at first had to be stopped. Of the initial recruits, 190 had been discharged and returned to work at the colliery and other men had also been recruited.

During the war underground wage costs had gone up by 114 per cent, surface wages by 160 per cent, charges for stores and materials by 147 per cent, but selling price by just 101 per cent. Production had also fallen by 32 per cent, but Orchard thought that considering the number of active men who had joined the army, that was not unsatisfactory. A pact with the miners' union had led to a strike-free time during the war, and Orchard said the the spirit of conciliation and forbearance would be neccessary to face the problems that lay ahead, and an atmosphere created not by sabre-rattling and mailed fists, but by a spirit of justice and goodwill. His wishes were not to be realised.

Miners' hopes for the post-war nationalisation of the industry were dashed and strikes in 1920 and 1921 left the industry weakened and morale at a low ebb. By 1922 the British coal industry was facing a serious crisis. Too little investment in mechanisation, overmanning, reduced output, loss of markets to the oil and electricity industries, and the decline of the export trade, had begun to have an enormous impact In his presidential address to the MGMS in May, 1922, Sydney A. Smith quoted many statistics in a rather gloomy survey of the industry. He warned that many of the older collieries were now becoming exhausted, and although there were large extensions of the coalfield still available for development, the seams were at great depth and would require great skill to exploit.

In 1838 when the Society was founded, total coal output for the entire country was about 30 million tons, compared with a peak in 1913 of 287m tons, and 229m tons in 1920. Coal exports from Britain had fallen from 73m tons in 1913 to some 25m tons in 1920. Over the same period manning had increased, with 1,127,800 people employed in 1913 and 1,248,224 people employed in 1920. Smith blamed the reduction in output on a cut-back in working hours and the two recent strikes. Neither did he see any hope in the unions' desire for nationalisaton of the industry, pointing out that all the current mines had been sunk with private capital and risks had been taken on development work which would not be undertaken by a Government department.

The strike in the autumn of 1920 had, said Smith, cost export orders which had now been placed with the United States, and the three-month strike in 1921 had caused incalculable loss to the owners and miners. Production costs had also soared with wages alone going up four-fold between 1913 and 1920. In 1913 it cost 8s 7 1/2d to produce a ton of coal, with wages accounting for 6s. 4d, other costs 2s. 3 1/2d and the owner adding a further 1s 6d a ton for profit. By 1920 it cost 34s. 1 1/4d to produce a ton of coal, with wages the major item at 25s. 9 1/2d, other costs at 8s 3 3/4d and owners' profit adding a further 2s. 6 1/2d. At the same time production had gone down from 259 tons a man in 1913 to 190 tons a man in 1920.

Smith thought it probable there would be very few new sinkings of collieries until labour and material costs were reduced. It was also essential, said Smith, that "permanent peace relations" should be established between employers and employed. "I have faith in the common sense of the British working man to arrange the differences that inevitably arise with his employer, but these should be settled locally, and not left in the hands of agitators who, after all, are only a small minority," he stated.

Smith ended his address with a staunch defence of private ownership of the pits. "In my judgement, and, I trust, unprejudiced consideration, the nationalisation of the collieries would check enterprise, particularly in the experimental proving, and the development of new coalfields, the establishment of new collieries and the development of the many by-industries now carried on in connection with the collieries. It would be most costly to the nation...by reducing both imperial and local revenue, disastrous to the other industries dependent upon cheap coal, and prejudicial to the best interests of the miners themselves," he concluded.

James Lomax: Pit to the Laboratory

A member of MGMS who gained an unusual niche in the scientific world was James Lomax (1857-1934). Although lacking formal training, he established a world-wide reputation for the preparation of thin sections of fossil plants and coal for microscopic study. Lomax claimed that he first went down a pit when he was three years old, but it was seven years later before he started work underground at Elton Collieries, Bury, where his father was manager. Lomax returned to school for two years at the age of 13 before returning to the pit. From

1876 to 1888 he worked as a winder and engineer, firstly at Clifton and Kersley Coal Company and later at Andrew Knowles and Son.

In 1933 members of the MGMS visited the Lomax Paleo-botanical Laboratories in Bolton, and Lomax gave a brief resume of his scientific life from his first days underground. "I was always looking out for fossils. In later years I obtained specimens from the roof and seams which I thought contained more in the interior than could be seen on the surface. I began to break them up and then rubbed them down to a flat surface and in this way I saw that fossil plants had some part of the vegetative or cellular tissue preserved. I seldom missed the opportunity of collecting fossil impressions of plants in the pit sinking or in tunnelling. My work included the petrifications in coal balls which I found to contain the cellular remains of the original plants that now constitute coal, and from these much has been learned about the structure of coal."

In 1885 Lomax began an association with Professor Williamson, of Owens College, and they became good friends. Lomax was interested in the stratigraphical sequence of the coal measures, and a note in the MGMS Transactions in 1933, when Lomax was made an Honorary Member, says that he and Williamson laid the foundation of knowledge of fossil plants based mainly on discoveries of types and species found in the Lancashire and Yorkshire coalfields.

In 1906, with the support of several academics, the Lomax Paleo-botanical Laboratory was established in Bolton, and Lomax began the difficult task of making thin sections in coal. Lomax described the long period of trial and error: "My investigations led me to believe that coal showed structure...and I tried to make sections of coal which would show this, but although everything that could be utilised for the purpose was tried I was unable to make a section any larger than a thumbnail. The chief difficulty was the evolution of gas when the specimen was mounted on a glass plate containing the heated medium.

"The trouble was solved in an almost tragic manner. Most of us remember the Christmas of 1910 when the deplorable explosion at Hulton Colliery occurred. I...rushed off to see whether I could make myself useful...when I left the pit in the afternoon trying to forget what had happened, I set to work on further experiments in order to make a satisfactory coal section. Before ten o'clock that night my work was complete and I had obtained a section about three inches square showing the position of flammable and other ingredients of the Plodder Seam, in which the explosion had occurred. The method evolved then is still, with slight alterations, in use today," said Lomax in 1933.

Lomax's early work on coal impressed colliery owners and his business eventually became associated with the Lancashire and

Cheshire Coal Research Association, a coal-owners organisation which carried out research into a variety of mining subjects. Lomax gave a large number of papers to learned societies, and photographs of thin sections were used to illustrate his papers in the MGMS Transactions. Samples of his work have survived and there is a collection in Bolton Museum.

CHAPTER NINE

Mechanisation and James Anderton

James Anderton

Mining was not exempt from the great strides made in industrial research and production methods during the First World War, and the MGMS Transactions from then until the present day show a great awareness of the technical needs of the industry. New solutions to old problems were sought to make mines safer and more productive, and the slow progress towards making the miner a machine operator rather than a pick-and-shovel labourer can be plotted through Society records.

The Society played a leading role soon after World War One in the formation of the Lancashire and Cheshire Safety in Mines Research Committee which over many years did valuable work for the industry, and papers on its findings were read to the Society. By the 1930s the research committee was composed of eight members of the MGMS, eight members nominated by the Lancashire and Cheshire Coal Research Association, two members from the Lancashire and Cheshire Miners' Federation and three co-opted members, who included Mr. W.J. Charlton, the Divisional Inspector of Mines.

The LCSMRC investigated many subjects of current concern to mining engineers, and in the early Thirties, with the mechanisation of coal faces increasing, the LCSMRC gave a series of papers on Gas Evolution and the Rate of Advance. A paper in January 1933 on Longwall Roof Control in the Arley Mine drew comparisons between roof conditions under machine mining compared to hand mining and observations were made in six different areas. Later papers from the committee included Runaways on Endless Over-rope Haulage, Plucking in Endless Ropes, Man-riding haulage in Lancashire, and in 1941 a report on experiences with reinforced concrete props at the coalface.

A paper on "Scraper-loaders, Conveyors, Intensive Methods of Mining and a New Method of Blasting Coal", which reflected the latest technology in the industry, was read to the Society in January, 1931, by Mr L C Maitland. In 1921 only 801 coalface conveyors were working in British collieries, but by 1929 the figure had grown to 2,598, 330 of which were in pits in Lancashire and North Staffordshire. Scraper-loading had been introduced into Britain from the USA only two years earlier, said Maitland, but its application had extended rapidly in coal seams varying in thickness from five feet down to 15-inches. There were, though, serious limiting factors in its use, and scraper-loaders could not be used where the floor was very soft, the roof was bad or where space between the props was not wide or straight enough to allow the scraper to travel across the face. There were difficulties too on long faces in thicker seams, where scraper-loading could not deal with the large outputs being dealt with by multiple face conveyors delivering into each other.

Miners, said Maitland, liked the scraper-loader because it took less physical energy to push coal three or four feet into the scraper track, rather than throwing coal into tubs or on to a face conveyor. Other advantages included that a scraper-loader could work uphill almost as easily as downhill; there was an increase of between five and ten per cent in large coal; output increased and costs were cheaper. The cost per ton to main haulage by using a scraper-loader was 3s.1 1/2d compared to almost 3s.10d on a longwall conveyor face.

In the Explosives in Coal Mines Order of 1930, the Cardox (Type G) carbon dioxide cartridge had been included in the permitted list. This, said Maitland, would lead to greater safety, more round and cleaner coal and increased production. In experiments at the Government testing station it had not been possible to cause an explosion in gas-filled chambers when firing a cartridge and as the pressure exerted by Cardox was one-eighth that of conventional explosives there was not the same shattering effect on the coal.

Another important advance in mining safety was the increasing use of steel roof supports at the working face, and in January, 1940, Mr J.F. Carr reported on the recent change from timber to steel. The advantages of steel were permanency and the elimination of the daily trouble and expense of transporting and handling large quantities of timber underground. Steel props and bars could be uneconomical if there was not efficient control and organisation but more steel props were lost by being laid on the floor and buried than by being left undrawn in the waste.

American mining techniques played an important role in the increasing mechanisation of the British industry during the Second World War, and in December, 1943, the IMinE published a major paper on "The American System of Coal-mining", by H.R. Wheeler, for discussion by the federated institutes. American machinery, such as Goodman Duckbill conveyors and Goodman Shortwall coal-cutters, together with increasing output from home manufacturers, was then being used in British mines, and in February, 1944, G.M. Gullick gave an overall review to the MGMS on the development of power-loading. Following the increased use of machinery, Gullick said it must fall upon management to meet the requirements of altering conditions of employment as well as in the science and art of mining; in other words, the industry would in future, as always in the past, look to the mining engineer for a solution to many of its problems. Looking to the future and problems such as thin seams, Gullick forecast "...that in due course types of loaders will be evolved to suit conditions for which nothing suitable exists today." It was to be just about ten years before the machine came along which was to revolutionise the winning of coal.

In October, 1954, James Anderton was elected President of the MGMS, and in his address gave a review of the geology and history of the St. Helens Coalfield, a subject on which he was uniquely qualified to comment. His family had been in the shaft sinking trade for generations, but his parents were at first determined not to let him enter the industry. Persuasion prevailed and at the age of 13 he began work as an office boy at the Maypole Colliery, Abram. In 1928, at the age of 23, he gained his First Class Certificate at Wigan Mining and Technical College, and was launched on an eminent career. He managed Maypole Colliery, Mains, Ince Moss and Clock Face, St. Helens, before becoming Production Manager, and, in 1949, General Manager of the St. Helens Area. In 1958, Anderton went to the Scottish Division of the National Coal Board as Deputy Chairman with responsibility for production and reconstruction before returning to Lancashire in 1961 as Chairman of the North Western Division.

One subject Anderton did not touch on during his presidential address was his major contribution to the post-war coal industry, and which, arguably, did more to raise production than any other single event - his invention of the Anderton shearer-loader, a machine which cuts and loads coal in one operation. The MGMS had to wait three months until January, 1955, before L.C. Timms and T. Lester gave a paper on the machines, one of which, at Wood Colliery in 1954, was cutting and loading about 5000 tons of coal a month. Remarkable as these figures were for their time, they pale in comparison to the outputs being achieved in 1987 by advanced shearer-loaders which can cut and load coal at a rate of some 1500 tons an hour, an enviable productivity record.

Timms and Lester said that by 1953, the post-war rate of improvement in coal production had begun to slow down, and it became obvious that improvement could only come from increased efficiency on the coalface. Difficult working conditions in the St Helens area had generally been considered unsuitable for armoured conveyors and power-loading, and a critical examination of all the power-loaders available had raised problems such as the floor being too soft, the seam height too variable or the coal too hard; and in every case there was the ever-present bogy of local faulting.

It was evident that a new machine was needed which was independent of roof or floor, small and easily manoeuvreable at faults, and capable of giving a steady flow of coal to the haulage. "Flexibility was what was wanted, so we set off to try and get it," Anderton told Coal Quarterly in 1964, and it was flexibility and comparative simplicity which made the shearer a world-wide success. "Conditions vary greatly in Britain's coalfields; even in the same coalfield there is no consistency. Varying hardnesses of coal, changing seam gradients , a wide range of roof and floor conditions, seams of different thicknesses from, say, thirty inches to eight feet or more: these and other variations present endless problems, and equipment designed for one set of conditions is usually unsuitable elsewhere," said the NCB magazine. "The Anderton Shearer is an exception. It is so adaptable that it can be used successfully in most of the conditions encountered in Britain. Which is remarkable in a machine initially designed to overcome specific geological problems in one area."

Anderton's first idea was to turn a coalcutter on its side and mount it on an amoured conveyor, so that the plane of the cut was vertical and a web of coal about one foot thick was taken off. The jib could be adjusted to trim the floor, and by adding another trailing jib, the roof coal could be trimmed down in a seam of varying thickness. This machine was tried in a seam six-feet thick but was rather cumbersome. The demand for simplicity then led to the idea which

Development of the shearer-loader. Above: An AB16, circa 1956, with one 80hp motor, and capable of cutting seams between 36 inches and 60 inches. Below: The AM500 double-ended ranging drum shearer of 1986, with two 500hp motors for working in seams up to 15-feet thick. *(Pictures: Anderson Strathclyde.)*

was to make the shearer-loader a success - the coalcutter gearhead was adapted to take a gearbox with a horizontal shaft, on which was mounted a vertical cutter disc.

The first machine was installed in July, 1952, in the Rushy Park seam at Ravenhead Colliery, St. Helens, followed by others at Cronton Colliery, St. Helens and Golborne Colliery, near Leigh. Anderton's first machines were developed not in a formal research and development department, but by NCB maintenance and workshop staff. An early, and lasting major improvement was the introduction of drums fitted with picks in place of the cutting disc. In 1954 there were 28 machines in use and two years later more than 200. The 1950s were a period of solving teething troubles, but by the mid-1960s well over 600 machines were producing coal in British collieries and output from shearer-loaders was greater than all other power-loaders put together.

Anderton's principle was quickly taken up by manufacturers of longwall coal cutting machines such as Anderson Boyes of Motherwell, Mavor and Coulson of Glasgow and British Jeffrey Diamond of Wakefield, who made fixed drum shearers with their own design details, capable of cutting and loading a web of coal some 20 inches wide. The idea was also adopted by manufacturers in France and Germany. With the earlier models, the web of coal was cut along the face followed by a "flitting" or cleaning-up passage of the machine, when any remaining cut coal lying on the floor was loaded on to the face conveyor by a plough arrangement attached to the shearer. These first machines, powered by 50 horsepower electric motors, were used in coal seams from 36 inches to 60 inches thick, with the diameter of the drum corresponding to the thickness of coal extracted. Compressed air motors were also available for gassy seams. In 1960 Anderson Boyes (now Anderson Strathclyde) had machines with 80 and 125 horsepower motors, and by 1963 a bi-directional shearer, with drums of up to 72-inches and webs of up to 30-inches, had been developed to work thicker seams.

Further development of Anderton's original concept brought, in 1963, a 200hp ranging-drum shearer incorporating an arm pivoted at the end of the gearhead and carrying the cutting drum, which was raised and lowered in a vertical plane. This gave greater flexibility than the fixed drum as the cutting drum could follow any undulations or variations in the seam, and thicker seams could be extracted by a two-pass method, using a drum smaller in diameter than the seam thickness. The ranging arm also allowed the cutting drum to be extended beyond the end of the face conveyor which simplified mining operations at the face ends. In 1965 Anderson Boyes had a 270 horsepower double-ended ranging shearer with a ranging arm and cutting drum at each end of the machine, allowing seams from five feet to ten feet thick to be extracted in a single-pass operation. By 1987, double-ended ranging drum shearers with two motors had an installed power of up to 1,000 hp, cutting and loading coal at up to 1500 tons or more an hour from seams of up to 15 feet thick. Built-in microprocessor based systems are used to steer these machines, monitor the condition of the machine's components and performance and transmit information to a surface control centre.

The number of shearers based on the Anderton principle in use in Britain peaked at around 900 in the mid-1970s, but with the contraction of the coal industry this figure had declined in 1987 to 480. In 1986 shearer-loaders produced 84.3 million tons of coal - 85.5 per cent of the total output from all longwall mechanised faces, and 80 per cent of the total output of coal. Not only has the industry in Britain been revolutionised, but every major coal-producing country in the world is now using shearer-loaders.

Anderton retired from the NCB in 1967 and joined Gullick Dobson, the Wigan firm of mining machinery manufacturers, as a consultant, a post he held until 1983. With his colleagues he worked on advanced roof support systems, an area which holds the key to the next big breakthrough in mining techniques - the totally automated coalface. Further advances of the coal producing system which combines the shearer-loader and powered supports with sophisticated control systems, anticipate the time when the average face will produce one million tons of coal a year.

The coal industry owes much to Anderton and his contribution was recognised in 1964 by the award of the Medal of the Institution of Mining Engineers "for outstanding services to coalmining, with particular reference to coalface mechanisation." An honorary member of the MGMS, he was awarded the CBE in 1964 and the Krupp Prize for Energy Research in 1979.

Roof Control Systems

Increasing mechanisation of the coalface focussed attention on the major problem of efficient roof control. In 1947, year of the nationalisation of the coal industry, the three-shift cycle of operations on longwall faces was common in most pits. Coal was pre-cut, drilled and blasted in the first shift before being hand-loaded on to a face conveyor, while the newly exposed roof was supported with hand-set wooden props and steel bars, a vital but time consuming and unproductive exercise. In the third shift the face conveyor was dismantled and manhandled closer to the advancing face. The introduction into British mines in 1947 of the "panzer", a flexible armoured conveyor, revealed, when run in tandem with a coalcutter, the possibilities and immense productivity benefits of the continuous coal-getting cycle on a coalface free of conventional props.

The idea of mechanised roof support was not new, and in a paper to the National Association of Colliery Managers in 1956, C. Trehearne Jones said at least one design had been put forward as early as 1912. In the years following the Second World War, British manufacturers rapidly introduced hydraulic power, and scored over their continental rivals, who preferred mechanical roof supports.

In a two-part paper to the MGMS branch in 1982, Alan Purdy looked back over the 25 years since the Wigan firm of Gullick Dobson had first introduced its first full face of powered roof supports. The company had been well placed to exploit the market in hydraulic equipment, for before the Second World War they had been involved in the development of James Tonge's "Coalburster", a hydraulic cartridge for breaking down coal without the use of explosives. Tom Seaman, a director of Gullick, had specialised in hydraulics and his idea of using water and soluble oil as a safe and cheap medium was an important factor in the design of the first hydraulic props.

In 1949 hydraulic rams were first introduced to push armoured conveyors closer to the face, and these were followed two years later by hydraulic props, into which rams were soon integrated. The hydraulic prop became an ideal support system by which to exploit the new prop-free front method of working, said Purdy, and soon mechanised support systems using link bars, then slide bars, eliminated most of the problems previously experienced with hand-set prop and bar support systems. In 1952 came a major breakthrough with the first "walking" hydraulic chock which was propelled forward by the ram. Four props were set in a box frame surmounted by a canopy on to which could be attached two steel bars to give forward support to the roof at the coal face. In June, 1954, 30 four-leg chocks were installed in the Low Main Seam at Ormonde Colliery, East Midlands, and were so successful that the entire face was equipped with the supports the following year.

This system, said Purdy, offered several advantages, including an improved caving line; a high setting and yield load to the roof and floor to prevent loss of roof control; the exposed area of roof from coal face to waste was less than with a prop and bar system, thus bringing caving (collapse of the roof in the waste) closer to the coal head; a prop-free front measurement of more than seven feet and the possibility of reducing manpower.

The Sixties, Purdy went on, brought about a rapid application of powered supports to coal faces, but by 1966 it had become apparent that although the mining systems being installed were .capable of producing at a very high rate, an overall improvement in running time had not been achieved. The emphasis on roof-support development then sought to make chocks stronger with larger bore legs and bigger yielding capacities, increased speed of operation and reliability of setting, and simple and fast maintenance. Stringent testing also paid dividends in the field of safety, and in 1979 it was reported that on British coalfaces there had been one fatality for every million shifts compared to 3.4 fatalities in France, 3.3 fatalities in the USA and 3 fatalities in Germany.

The next stride forward in roof control came with the shield support, a type developed in Russia in the 1950s for use in seams in excess of two metres and having friable roof conditions. Early models were not without significant problems, but in 1964 a full-face installation was bought by the NCB and fitted with Gullick valve gear. This installation never went underground, and it was not until 1970 when a German face was installed with shields, that their advantage over conventional chocks became widely acknowledged. Advantages of the shields were better resistance to lateral loading; increased stability and the elimination of leg support towers which led to better ventilation and unobstructed travel ways. The first shields were of a single-pivot caliper design but following extensive design work the lemniscate linkage was developed. This was a double link arrangement between base and rear shields which let the canopy converge almost vertically while still retaining a resistance to lateral loadings. The first British pit to have shield supports was Saville Colliery, Yorkshire, in August 1976 when nine Dowty 2-leg shields were installed. The first Gullick Dobson shield trials were in a mine in Utah, USA, in October 1976, and at Rossington Colliery in January, 1978.

In 1985, Frank Jones chose the evolution of roof control support systems for his keynote speech as President of the MGMS Branch. "The rapid development of the powered support, and the modern control valve system based on the microchip, will further release the potential of the powered support at a time when the industry needs a reduction in production costs and the ability to compete with other major energy sources," said Jones. "British control systems are already doing just this in the USA and Australia and this could well be the norm for the next decade."

Like the shearer-loader, which was developed in parallel with the powered support, British mining technology in the field of strata control has been a world-wide success and has gained export markets.

Industrial Relations

The introduction of advanced machinery was not the only major challenge facing mining engineers in the years following nationalisation. The conflicting roles of men and owners, established over many earlier decades, could no longer be accepted in the modern industry and improved industrial relations became a priority. James C. Fletcher, in his presidential address in 1958, appealed for closer co-operation between men and management and suggested that the deputies' association and the miners' union be invited to become subscribers to the Institution and have the right to send two members to meetings.

As coal came under increasingly greater threat from oil, natural gas and nuclear energy, modern management techniques became increasingly important. In his presidential address to the MGMS in

1961, George W. Sanders said the dominant issue facing the industry was the development, efficient utilisation and conservation of manpower, the industry's most valuable asset, next to its mineral reserves. The most acute danger at that time was that mining techniques were rapidly outstripping the development of human organisation, capacity and attitudes within the industry, with the result that the best use was not being made of greatly improved production facilities. The industry had received a severe shock in 1957, said Sanders, when over-production forced the NCB to restrict recruitment, curtail student education and close a number of collieries. This had led to continuing wastage of operatives and recruitment had declined. It was also alarming to see young men of tremendous potential leaving the industry because they could not be given the chance to use their training. At the other end of the scale, senior executives were worn out long before their time.

The task of the mining engineer in 1961, said Sanders, was to organise production so that confidence was restored and morale raised so that operatives would enter or remain in the industry in greater numbers. The only way to remain in business with a dwindling and increasingly expensive workforce, he went on, was to replace muscle with brains and horsepower. But even this policy would not be sufficient unless power-loading installations were carefully planned with adequate supporting facilities, and that the dynamic organisation of the industry kept pace with rapidly-changing techniques.

The changing face of the industry was also a theme in the presidential address to the Society by L. R. Boyfield in October, 1964. The amount of coal obtained from power-loaders had increased from 8.3 per cent in 1954 to 68.4 per cent in 1964, and the advent of the narrow-web power-loader, together with the introduction of powered supports, presented the mining engineer with a breakthrough in production.

Towards the end of the 1960s, contraction of the coal industry in the face of competition, together with pit closures due to exhaustion of reserves, brought new worries, particularly to the Lancashire coalfield. W. Bibby, President in 1968-69, told the Society there was a feeling of apprehension and uncertainty about the future. Government policy on fuel had also made it imperative to accelerate the closure programme to avoid increasing coal stocks in a changing market, but this had brought serious concern about redundancies which in turn had undermined the confidence of all those in the industry. In a wide-ranging review he suggested a number of ways in which the current problems could be tackled.

Throughout the Seventies and Eighties, the coal industry faced increasingly difficult economic times, and presidents of the MGMS Branch repeatedly drew attention to the role to be played by effective management. K. Moses told the Branch in 1971, that still persisting was "the old problem" of producing enough coal at the right price for the market and which would yield reasonable wages and a fair profit on capital invested. Modern economic events, both within the industry and outside, had created additional problems for mining engineers whose role had always been onerous and who "must at once be the leader, the co-ordinator, (and) the innovator. His has always been the task of leading the industry toward higher standards of performance," he said.

In October, 1976, C. Daniels said that in his 28 years experience in management the most important internal policy changes had been the run-down in global tonnages, the expansion in mechanisation and the change to the day-wage system of payment. "The evolution of these events when interrelated has caused a progression of changes in the attitudes of workers, and in the means of motivation used by management to influence the effects of the changing attitudes..." In a comprehensive outline of the functions of management, Daniels said as the techniques of mining engineering continued to change, the manager would have to continue to influence human beings in such a way as to fulfill objectives, while complying with an ever-changing set of rules and external influences. "But as basic human behaviour will never change, so then the techniques of managing men successfully will never change," he added.

A year later, William Shawcross spoke of the effect that education, social changes and legislation had played in shaping attitudes of the modern workforce. A better informed workforce would create a demand for change, and management needed to be involved in creating acceptance of new situations and influencing the end product. "Unless this is done there is danger that imposed arrangements, dictated by political dogma, will be the order of the day. If this was so, it would only add further to the frustrations of management without effectively recognising and acting upon the fundamental causes of industrial stagnation," he went on.

Another success story in which mining engineers played a major role over past decades is in the great strides made in the field of safety. The introduction of new technology has been important, with automatic gas detection and roof support equipment being two of the most vital areas of development. In his presidential address in 1975, W. Holdsworth pointed out that fatalities in the industry had fallen from 1,785 in 1913 to 612 in 1947. Of the 56 deaths recorded in 1974-75, 18 had been in the haulage and transport areas, and 13 in falls of ground. Nevertheless, said Holdsworth, mining was still hazardous and in looking forward to the possibility of a year with no fatalities it was important to simultaneously deal with other accidents. In 1974-75 there had been 576 serious reportable accidents and 54,333 other accidents.

Mechanisation of the coalface had been a major objective of the drive to improve output, and by the 1980s mining engineers could reflect on more than three decades of advancement. Progress in that area had, however, highlighted serious problems elsewhere. In his 1983 Presidential Address, D. Hardman concentrated on EBG - improving efficiency Elsewhere Below Ground. "There is ... an inarguable case ... that the future of the industry depends heavily on the extent to which efficiency outbye of the face can be increased," he claimed.

Neither was EBG a minor preoccupation, for it could involve such major reorganisation as the amalgamation of collieries to concentrate output at a single outlet, while retaining other services at outlying shafts. Other areas for improvement were underground roadways and drivages, and the installation and salvage of coalface equipment. In the longer term, said Hardman, the aim must be for virtually manless coal clearance systems; elimination of the manual handling of materials, equipment and vehicles; the extension and improvement of manriding systems and further reductions of hazards to safety.

By the mid-1980s coal faced an increased financial crisis following the strike of 1983-84 and a collapse in energy prices. "EBG efficiency still remains a critical factor in our overall success," stated G. W. Mapp, British Coal's Western Area Transport Development Engineer, in a 1986 review of the previous three dramatic years. Any strategy aimed at obtaining lower production costs, said the President, had to include fewer faces

CHAPTER TEN

Firedamp and Safety Lamps

"Now this invisible and intangible enemy is...
dangerous to the coal miner, often coming suddenly
upon him, like a thief in the night."
                                        –E.W. Binney, 1861

Many are the lectures and discussions recorded in the Transactions of the Manchester Geological Society on the perils of firedamp, or methane gas, in coal workings. As the industry expanded and collieries became larger, so did the human toll rise as explosions ripped through workings with fearful loss of life and injury. The problem of providing safe lighting for men working in gas-filled strata had taxed many scientific minds. Even before the first safety lamps had been introduced, the phosphorescent rotting skins of fish had been used to provide a faint glimmer of light underground.

Amongst the pioneers of lighting devices was the Reverend Carlisle Spedding who invented a steel mill operated by a boy and which provided a shower of sparks. The dangers were obvious, for the sparks could ignite methane and even under safe conditions the light produced was minimal. In 1815 a safety lamp invented by Dr E. Clanny was the first to be taken underground into an explosive atmosphere without incident. This lamp, together with Clanny's second design, was totally unsuitable for practical work, being too clumsy and requiring the full-time attentions of a man to operate a pair of bellows which pumped air to the flame.

There were major breakthroughs in 1816 with both Sir Humphrey Davy and George Stephenson, the railway engineer, inventing lamps which were to provide the basis for the development of oil-fuelled safety lamps over the rest of the century. Davy's success was in discovering that flame would not pass through a wire gauze and in its most basic form his lamp consisted of a cylinder of gauze attached to an oil-burner at its base.

Stephenson's "Geordie" lamp was based on the observation that flames did not pass through tubes of a certain diameter, and his first lamp consisted of a glass cylinder with perforated metal cap to allow hot air to escape, and a number of perforations in the base to let in fresh air. The lamp was then encased with a metal shield with holes to allow light out. Clanny also persisted with his experiments and an improved design became popular and the source of much development.

A major feature of the safety lamp was its use to detect firedamp and this won it the Latin motto of "Moneo et Munio" - I warn and I protect. However, flame safety lamps could in some instances be treacherous allies and caution against misplaced trust was urged by some engineers and coal owners, including Binney. Until quite late in the 19th Century these views were generally overwhelmed by uncritical support for lamps amongst the practical mining fraternity. There had been serious doubts about the total safety of flame lamps as early as the 1830s and a three-year investigation into an explosion at St. Hilda's Colliery by the South Shields Committee declared that the Davy lamp was absolutely unsafe.

In 1861 there were a number of discussions on safety lamps at meetings of the Manchester Geological Society, with Binney showing considerable anxiety over the conditions in which lamps could be considered safe and whether a lamp could explode in gassy conditions. Binney did not detail why he thought lamps might be dangerous, and said the cause of ignition of explosions often remained a matter of conjecture, for "In the majority of cases no man is left to tell the tale."

The dangers of using safety lamps in currents of air which could blow the flame through the gauze had been expressed but were little appreciated, and there was at that time a general feeling amongst coal owners - and the Mines Inspectorate - that a well-maintained lamp was safe in gas. Neither was it considered necessary to have lamps in general use and for many decades of the 19th Century naked lights were very common underground.

In April, 1861, Andrew Knowles told the Society that safety lamps should be used only where danger could be proved. "Many mines make firedamp during the time the straight work is being driven, and when that is finished get drained of gas and may then be worked with open lights," he told a Society meeting. "Before compelling the men to work a coal mine with the use of safety lamps, it should be ascertained to be dangerous; because it is a great hardship to a collier to make him work with a lamp which gives worse light than a candle," added the coal owner.

Knowles had pinpointed one of the major faults of safety lamps - the very poor light they emitted. Disastrous as explosions could be, colliers felt that candles had a safety aspect insomuch as they could identify potential falls of roof and sides easier than with a safety lamp which generally gave off less than half a candlepower of light. The better light of the candle also increased productivity, and earnings.

Also in 1861, Binney criticised the inventor of a safety-lamp locking device who had claimed there was no evidence of an explosion in a proper lamp. "I say there are many instances," said Binney, "The inventor of the Davy lamp ....always cautioned people not to move the lamp against a current of air. He never expected there would be coal dust accumulated on the wire gauze, and then oil spilled upon such coal dust, and the lamp, without being cleaned, allowed to become full of flame".

Even when safety lamps were being used in well ventilated and gas-free conditions, the situation could be transformed rapidly. The emission of gas into working places was not always as stealthy as suggested by the quotation at the beginning of the chapter. If colliers struck a pocket of methane the gas could erupt into the workings with the ferocity of a fractured high pressure steam pipe.

One incident of such a blower at Kirkless Hall Colliery, Wigan, was described to the Society in February, 1861, by Peter Higson, an Inspector of Mines. The outburst was so great as to overcome the ventilation; more than 350 men had to be hastily evacuated from the pit, and 1000 yards of intake course remained gas-logged for up to 18 hours. "I attribute the safety of the men in this instance to the lamps throughout the entire colliery, being in a state of perfect repair," said Higson, who later inspected the source of the outburst and found a rip in the floor between the goaf and coal face some 30 or 40 yards long in which he could put his arm up to the shoulder.

Badly maintained safety lamps or lamps which could be opened by careless colliers underground were as great a menace as open lights. In April, 1861, Joseph Dickinson said it had been the practice to let a man go into a mine with his own lamp in whatever state it might be. "I have seen some with picker holes in them large enough to pass a pencil through. I have seen a manager with his gauze without a hoop; and a fireman's lamp with a gauze of only 256 meshes to an inch instead of 784," said the Mines Inspector.

In May, 1861, Joseph Goodwin, of Hyde and Haughton Collieries, wrote to the Society denying that a Davy lamp could explode in gas and he instanced an occasion when a miner at Norberry Colliery had thrown a burning Davy lamp many yards. "The space through which the lamp passed when thrown was completely filled with gas, yet it did not cause an explosion," wrote Goodwin. He accepted that the safety lamp had valuable use for the detection of gas, but even if it could be made absolutely perfect, so that explosions would be rendered impossible, he was not in favour of it being use exclusively underground.

"Unless some corresponding care was taken to ensure perfect ventilation to clear the mine of all the deleterious gases that are generated ....I should consider it one of the greatest calamities that could befall the coalminer to make the lamp perfect and to use it exclusively," said Goodwin, adding, "If you have ever ... noticed the men that have worked for a few years with the safety lamp, where it is used exclusively, you will have seen premature old age and decay stamped upon every lineament of the countenance of those who have scarcely arrived at the prime of life."

An Editor's footnote to this letter in the Transactions exposes the fatal flaw in the argument that many coal owners and miners used to express their faith in a glowing red-hot lamp even in a gas-filled atmosphere. The note states: "Dr. Wm. Gregory ... speaking of the mixture of light carburreted hydrogen and oxygen, which usually goes by the name of firedamp, says - If the air is less than six times, or more than fourteen times the volume of the gas, explosion does not take place." That is, if there was too little or too much methane in the air then there would not be an explosion even if a lamp was in flames or a naked candle was being used.

There are many recorded instances of lamps glowing red hot as methane, in heavily saturated atmospheres, burned within the gauze even when the wick had been turned fully down, but if a blazing lamp was carried into a workway with a reasonable amount of ventilation and an explosive concentration of gas, an explosion would have been inevitable.

It was later to be generally accepted that a concentration of between approximately five and 15 per cent of methane in the atmosphere would be explosive, with just over nine per cent being the most volatile. These figures were remarkably close to those of Doctor Gregory. It was also to be accepted that the various flame lamps were safe only provided air velocity did not exceed various limits. The basic Davy was considered unsafe if air movement exceed six feet per second; the basic Clanny at eight feet per second; the Stephenson at 13 feet per second; Mueseler at 21 feet per second; and two later lamps, the bonneted Mueseler and the Marsault at 40 feet per second.

Changing Opinions

In 1861 Joseph Dickinson praised the Davy lamp for its value in detecting gas in workings, and confidently told the Society: "I think we have arrived as nearly to the safe working of a mine as we can be expected to do." Dickinson's opinion, together with those of other fulsome advocates of flame safety lamps, was to change over the next 20 years as scientific investigation put substance into the misgivings of Binney and others.

An indication of how much times had changed came in December, 1877, when Dickinson lectured on the Davy lamp and Blasting in Mines. His opening words were: "The Davy lamp is known to be safe only under certain conditions." A man working in gassy conditions was now enjoined by Special Colliery Rules to smother out a flaring safety lamp. "If water were near he might probably dip it in, or if dust, cover it, or put it in his woollen jacket. Under such circumstances there is some risk," he told the Society. The Davy lamp was popular in the Lancashire coalfield, and despite its self-extinguishing properties, the Stephenson lamp had drawbacks which greatly restricted its general use.

Dickinson reviewed the requirements under the Coal Mines Acts for regular inspections for gas, the banning of all lights except locked safety lamps in places where there was likely to be an accumulation of gas and the storage of explosives. By this time there were Special Rules governing the use of lamps, and smoking had been banned except where naked lights were allowed. Lampmen were also to be employed to daily examine and lock each lamp before use.

In 1878 two Lancashire mining engineers, William Smethurst and James Ashworth began a series of experiments on various safety lamps, and the following spring they reported their principal findings to the Society. Their conclusions included an opinion that the Davy lamp, as ordinarily constructed, was not safe in coal mines giving out firedamp: particularly as gassy mines required better ventilation which increased air velocities and made the lamps more dangerous.

An ideal lamp, they concluded, would give the maximum quantity of light and should have a simple but effective lock which would extinguish the light if the lamp were opened. The lamp should be self-extinguishing in an explosive atmosphere, and the lamps should be filled and cleaned at the colliery and given to the workmen ready for use. The best lamp Smethurst and Ashworth tested was the Belgian-designed Mueseler, which gave a good steady light and was the best for proving a small percentage of gas in the atmosphere.

Ashworth and Smethurst's report was sent to the North of England Institute of Mining and Mechanical Engineers to be discussed, with other reports, at a meeting of mining societies and coal owners in February, 1879. The meeting was cancelled when the Government stepped into the growing debate over safety and announced the setting up of the Mines Accidents Commission, which conducted safety lamp

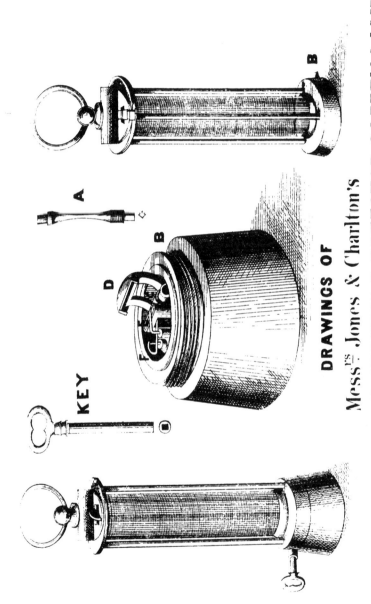

KEY

DRAWINGS OF

Messrs. Jones & Charlton's

PATENT SELF-EXTINGUISHING & DETECTOR SAFETY-LAMP,

for working miners

Geo. Charlton
Patentee, Manchester

experiments using Smethurst's equipment at Garswood Hall Collieries.

By the late autumn of 1880 the Commission told the Home Secretary that the Davy and Clanny lamps were unsafe in currents of explosive atmosphere of six feet per second unless they were protected by a shield of metal or glass. The Commission also acknowledged a report by Joseph Dickinson who had declared "that it was by no means well known that the Davy and Clanny lamps were unsafe in explosive currents." The result of this activity was to be a growing awareness for the use of safer lamps for miners, but even then some coal owners were not convinced of the neccessity for their sole use.

In 1885 Joseph Dickinson decreed that naked lights should not be used in his area following an explosion at Clifton Hall Colliery in which 122 men died. This led to a prolonged conflict with Herbert Fletcher, owner of Ladyshore Colliery at Little Lever and a fellow member of the Manchester Geological Society, who claimed that efficient ventilation and the tight packing of the goaf made naked lights safe.

Fletcher's theory does not seem to have been related to cost saving but rather an attempt to make working conditions better for miners. Fletcher thought that if the gas risk could be eliminated then miners would find it easier to work with candles which gave off more than twice the light of safety lamps. With better light, the risk of injury from falls of roof or sides would also be reduced, said supporters of the naked light theory. Although Fletcher's Ladyshore Colliery did not suffer a major explosive disaster there were at least two accidents involving gas during the years 1870-86, with one man being killed and several others injured.

After the explosion at Clifton Hall Colliery all the colliery owners in Dickinson's division, with the exception of Herbert Fletcher, agreed to use safety lamps exclusively. On May 3, 1886, Dickinson served a notice ordering Fletcher to stop the practice. Arbitration meetings were held at Bolton and Manchester before an award was made in support of Dickinson. In December, 1886, Fletcher lost an appeal in the High Court and by December 24 the Inspector of Mines had made another visit to Ladyshore to find candles still being used. After legal argument, proceedings were again started against Fletcher at the end of March, 1877, and he was later fined £20.

At an 1889 meeting of the Manchester Geological Society, Fletcher gave a paper on "The Effect of Goaf Stowage on Sudden Issues of Gas and on Ventilation." Dickinson was amongst those present. Fletcher quickly tried to refute arguments against his method of stowing waste, and spent considerably longer in extolling its virtues. He referred to nine of the most recent serious explosions in the Lancashire coalfield, and claimed that with only one partial exception, none of the collieries involved had practised packing of the waste. In five of the nine explosions he claimed that safety lamps were used exclusively, and in all the accidents he said it was the ventilation system which had been deficient.

Fletcher detailed wage rates at Ladyshore to prove to penny-conscious mine owners that packing the waste was not needlessly expensive even though all the wood props in the waste were left standing. "Only the pitmen amongst us who have used both (safety lamps and naked lights) can duly appreciate the great store set on their candles by pitmen at their work," Fletcher told the Society. "It is neither good engineering nor good political economy to shackle industries. The lamp is a shackle to the coalgetter ...while to the manager...it saves him the taking of many precautions, the observance of which would often interfere with his meeting the fluctuating demands of the market," he added.

As Fletcher ended his lecture, Joseph Dickinson proposed a vote of thanks , before pointedly remarking that he did not think many would support Fletcher in his view of working with candles in firedamp mines. "A poor light has always been put forward as being likely to cause a great increase in the number of accidents by falls...but we may expect to more than counter-balance it by the saving in the number of accidents from explosions," said Dickinson.

Fletcher does not seem to have been impressed by the counter argument and not many months after the MGS meeting he was again fined £20 for allowing naked lights to be used underground.

Safer Lamps

Agitation for safer lamps continued and the Coal Mines Act of 1887 decreed that lamps should "be so constructed that they may be safely carried against the air current ordinarily prevailing in that part of the mine in which the lamps are...in use even though such current should be inflammable." John S. Burrows, manager of Fletcher Burrows and Company's mines in Atherton, told the Society in November, 1890, that this was a very severe test for a lamp which required oxygen to support combustion and could not be hermetically sealed from the surrounding atmosphere.

To meet the new specifications Mueseler, Marsaut and other safer lamps were introduced, but they needed careful maintenance and Burrows remarked, "...a lamp cannot truly be called a safety lamp which depends for its safety on the most unremitting personal care and attention, and which in the absence of such care is simply a naked light."

Electric safety lamps were an obvious answer to the problems posed by the flame lamp, but their introduction proved difficult for a number of reasons. The first models weighed some 17lbs due mainly to the weight of the battery; initially there was the problem of light fading towards the end of a shift as the battery ran out; there was a problem with acid leakage; they were comparatively expensive and reliability could be suspect.

In December, 1888, John Burrows gave a report on working with the Edison Swan Portable Electric Mining Lamp, which had been used at Atherton Collieries for just over a year. The weight of the unit had been drastically reduced due to battery development, and weighed seven to eight pounds. Burrows praised the amount of light produced by that model and said it had proved popular with colliers. "To give a very rough idea of its lighting power, the lamp is better for seeing objects straight before one, than four large Marsaut lamps." Burrows had used an electric lamp to inspect a roof 14 feet high and could distinguish the slightest uneveness or break.

When in perfect order the lamp would give a good light for ten hours, could be turned upside down and dust, heat, draught or knocks made no difference to its output. "If such a lamp were adopted in our collieries, accidents would diminish very rapidly, explosions could hardly occur, unless the gas were fired by a shot, and men would not be found working under dangerous roof, or in insufficiently propped and spragged places, when the full extent of the danger was apparent," said Burrows.

There were disadvantages with the lamps in their current state of development, the principle one being the price. "Three guineas retail and two guineas wholesale per lamp, seems a fabulous sum for a lamp which is very simple in construction and which contains no expensive parts," he commented. There were also problems with the construction of the lamp and much time could be wasted in replacing a wire corroded by the leakage of acid, a common occurrence. A switch on the back of the battery box was also liable to damage. Burrows recommended that the oak battery cases, which were destroyed by acid, should be replaced with a case in papier-mache or similar material; a lid on top of the case should be easy to open so that faulty battery plates could be easily replaced and connecting wires should be outside the case. Cost needed to be reduced and battery plates and other spares made available to collieries so that lamps could be repaired on site and not sent back to the makers.

"There is no fault to find with the behaviour of the Edison Swan lamp when in good order, and it only rests with the makers to adopt the tradesmen's motto, "small profits and quick returns," at the same time simplifying the construction and supplying all parts needed for repairs. When this is done the electric lamp will soon take its place as the lamp for underground work," said Burrows.

Burrows' enthusiasm for the electric lamp was to be tempered with practical disadvantage and in his presidential address to the MGS in 1890, he said that the great hopes placed in the first portable electric lamps a year or two earlier, had not been fulfilled. The major problem remained the effect of the acid spilling from batteries and corroding electric connectors. By this time lighting with incandescent lamps on the surface and pit bottom was reasonably common, and Burrows, apparently having now abandoned the portable lamp to await improved models, had plans to illuminate a few working places by running 110 volt cables further underground.

With the vast potential market of the British coal industry waiting for a reliable electric hand lamp, manufacturers worked diligently to overcome initial difficulties and inroads gradually began to be made. Even so the flame lamp continued to be developed and in June, 1910, Mr. T. R. Stopford described to the Society a modification to the Marsaut lamp, based on the original Davy Lamp.

Early electric lamps were predominantly of the lead-acid type, and in January 1920 an electrical engineer, Mr William Maurice, told the Society of some of the problems which had been associated with them - poor accumulators, flimsy shells and fittings, unreliable bulbs and bad contact plates. While the batteries were being charged hydrogen gas was given off and this brought a risk of serious fires in lamphouses.

An alternative to lead-acid batteries came from nickel-iron cells and nickel-cadmium cells. In 1913 the Wolf Safety Lamp Company introduced an alkaline nickel-cadmium lamp which had shown unusual promise, but the outbreak of the First World War stopped production and halted the supply of spare parts. An improved Wolf lamp introduced after the war offered a large number of benefits, including being built of incombustible materials; the electrolyte had no corrosive action on the metal parts of the lamp; no gases were given off during discharge; the working life of a nickel-cadmium cell was at least 2,000 eight-hour shifts compared with 300 shifts for a lead-acid cell; alkaline cells could be charged quickly and their average candle power was higher than was usual with a lead-acid cell. Alkaline lamps were more expensive to buy than lead-acid lights, but taking maintenance costs into account, they were claimed to be cheaper in the long term.

In 1911 the Home Office organised a competition for the development of a safe portable electric miner's lamp, and one prize winner was the Lancashire firm of Oldham and Son, now Oldham

Batteries, of Denton. Oldham and Son had close connections with the mining industry as manufacturers of a steam dryer, a portable brake jig pulley and experimental coalcutter, and by the end of the First World War had supplied more than half of the 250,000 battery handlamps in use in collieries.

A major development of battery lamps between the wars was the introduction of cap lamps and by the mid-1950s these accounted for more than 90 per cent of the lamps used underground.

Gas Detection

The flame safety lamp was invaluable for detecting significant amounts of firedamp, but difficulties arose when the 1911 Coal Mines Act made requirements for the detection of amounts as low as one-quarter of one per cent. The Act also demanded that when one and a quarter per cent of methane was found in the atmosphere electrical power had to be cut off, and when two and a half per cent of firedamp was detected men had to be withdrawn from the affected workings. The flame lamp could not easily give readings of such accuracy. In 1926, Wigan Mining and Technical College conducted research into "Firedamp and its Detection", and came to the conclusion that the flame lamp was still the safest and most reliable method for routine testing for inflammable gas, but that accurate measurement required sampling and analysis on the surface, a procedure which could take from several hours to several days.

These conclusions led to Colin McLuckie, a lecturer at the Wigan College and a member of the MGMS, inventing a portable and safe methane meter which would give an accurate reading within a few minutes. McLuckie's device was based on the theory that a quantity of methane and air brought into contact with a glowing wire is converted into steam and carbon dioxide, with a resultant reduction in pressure. The new gas detector had two small chambers, one containing a platinum wire connected to a two-volt battery which burned the sample and the other a compensating chamber to eliminate errors due to temperature and pressure. A calibrated U-tube containing a coloured liquid connected the two chambers, and acted as a water-gauge to measure difference in pressure between the two compartments. The MGMS was given a demonstration of the detector in March, 1930, a few months before McLuckie gave a paper to the Mining Institute of Scotland.

In the 1980s gas detectors have moved into the realms of advanced technology, with transducers monitoring methane, carbon dioxide, products of combustion and air velocity in the underground environment and transmitting information to a surface control room. The pressure and purity of methane drained from the coal, often itself a valuable source of energy, and even fan vibration and dust flows in auxiliary ventilation systems can be monitored. These systems give mining engineers a round-the-clock check on mine ventilation and an increase in safety on modern faces with high outputs. Despite these advances, the flame lamp, more than 170 years after Davy and Stephenson made their prototypes, still has a critical role for methane detecting in coalmines. Current legislation determines the locations where lamps are used and the number employed. On a longwall face, for instance, one flame lamp is required for every eight men, and one lamp is required in each tunnel or heading or in a return airway where repairs are being carried out. Men carrying lamps are legally bound for their care and the actions to be taken when certain situations arise.

It is a tribute to W. E. Garforth, a former president of the MGMS and a pioneer of mining safety, that the Protector Lamp and Lighting company, of Eccles, still makes a "Garforth" flame lamp for gas testing.

CHAPTER ELEVEN

Education in Mining

"...discussions on safety lamps, sudden outbursts of
firedamp, ventilation in mines and on subjects of a kindred
nature, have... done good directly and they cannot fail to
prove of great advantage... by stimulating practical men to
the exercise of habits of vigilant and accurate
observation."–*MGS Council report, November, 1861.*

Manchester Geological and Mining Society, has, since its
foundation, show great interest in industrial education and
the safety of men working in the coal industry. Concern at the
number of miners killed and injured in explosions led to the instruction
of working miners on the use of safety lamps and the hazards of gas,
both explosive and toxic.

At its first meeting the members voted to allow ordinary miners
to become special members without having to pay subscription fees,
although there is no evidence that any colliers joined on this basis.
Anxiety was expressed at a meeting in October, 1841, about "the
fearful loss of life that annually takes place in this County from the
explosion of inflammable gases in coal mines." It was a subject which
forced itself on to the serious concern of the Society.

"Although the adventurous miner from the nature of his
employment, in dispute of all human care and foresight, must always
be subject to some danger in working the mineral treasures which
contribute very largely to the prosperity of our country, still it is
conceived that the dreadful catastrophes which so frequently occur
may with proper care be greatly diminished," said a Council report. "It
is but too clear in many instances, a great sacrifice of valuable lives has
originated either from the negligence of the owners or overlookers of
mines, or from the carelessness and ignorance of the working miners.
To remedy the first cause, of course, is the province of the legislature,
this Society can merely appeal to the humanity and interest of the
proprietors. But the other causes alluded to they cannot but consider

113

that it is their duty, if it be not in their power, to attempt to remove," the statement continued.

To achieve this object it was planned to instruct miners in the nature and properties of the gases found in mines; the causes of their generation and accumulation; the structure and principles of the different safety lamps and the circumstances under which lamps were safe - or dangerous. The Society asked Francis Looney, a man eager to spread the scientific word, to visit various parts of the coalfield to deliver lectures to miners, but his first attempt had to be postponed because of a strike over wages.

Looney began his tour in 1842 and attracted large crowds to his talks. He first visited Miles Platting where he spoke before 300 people, about a third of them colliers. At Flowery Field Sunday School, Hyde, "many respectable coal owners attended," but the number of miners was not as great as it might have been. At Dukinfield, in a room provided by the Dukinfield Coal Company, Looney spoke before 200 colliers who were shown a new, and apparently dangerous lamp. A long discussion took place about the lamp which was "proved to be totally inefficient." Another crowded audience at Oldham was shown the advantages of increased light from a double-wick safety lamp designed by Cornelius Backhouse. Again many coal owners attended the meeting.

Other packed meetings were held at Rhodes Mechanics Institute in Middleton, at Irlams o'th Heights, and in Sir Francis Egerton's school on Walkden Moor, where colliers again took part in a long discussion. At Looney's eighth and last meeting, at Clifton, there were several women in the audience, even though women were not allowed to work underground at the local colliery owned by the trustees of the late Ellis Fletcher. The meetings were also of benefit to Looney who would listen to his audiences who "furnished him with many valuable facts relative to the lamps now in use." In October, 1843, the Geology Society recommended that the lectures should continue with renewed energy, but unfortunately, Looney, who had quite a humble job, could no longer carry on and the initiative faded away.

Looney had a missionary zeal for the education of working people and the furtherance of science. Like other of his contemporaries in the Geological Society, he had been an active member of the Mechanics Institute. In his great desire to spread the benefits of education he toured towns surrounding Manchester giving lectures on geology, botany and natural history. So popular were Looney's Sunday lectures, said the Manchester Guardian in his obituary, that on one occasion clergymen tried to stop him hiring a room because he was luring away most of their congregations.

He was one of the first geologists to make a study of the Lancashire coalfield and detailed marine shells found above the lower coal measures, having one, Goniatites Looneyi, named after him. He also compliled a list of the shells and plant fossils of the coalfield which was published with an introduction to Elias Hall's geological map of the area. Looney did not sever his connections with the Society when the series of lectures ended and in December, 1843, he gave his "Observations on Safety Lamps and the Anemometer." The following February he was made an honorary member.

The Society's interest in mining education continued, and at the annual meeting in 1843 concern was expressed at the lack of Government interest in establishing a school of mining, "nothwithstanding she (Great Britain) owes nearly all her manufacturing and commercial greatness to her mineral resources." It was to be another 14 years before the Wigan Mining and Technical College was founded. The 1843 annual report again urged that coal masters and intelligent workmen should be invited to present practical knowledge to the Society and this would give geologists many scientific facts which they currently lost from the want of an opportunity of meeting together. It was a wish not to be fulfilled.

The Society regretted they had still not been able to attract coal owners to the meetings to discuss the phenomena of the Lancashire coalfield, but undeterred they planned, in 1844, to try and determine the range of the major faults, trace the direction in which seams of coal divided and ascertain the correct distances between certain beds. There was an eagerness to advance knowledge of mine working, and the most popular lecture in 1845, the year of a disastrous explosion at Haswell Colliery, was on mine ventilation.

Over the years as the Society changed its character and became predominantly a mining institute, the general meetings became a lecture room for the advancement of mining knowledge, with an ever-increasing proportion of the papers dwelling on industrial topics. Advances in safety lamps, ventilation, explosives, coal-getting machinery, and the advantages of longwall mining over pillar and stall, were amongst the subjects frequently and repeatedly discussed. The Society's library was a valuable asset to mining engineers and papers exchanged with mining institutes both in Britain and several countries abroad, brought a wealth of valuable information into Manchester.

In July, 1892, the Lancashire County Council Technical Instruction Committee asked for the Society's views on the requirements of the mining industries and the best method of providing technical instruction for miners. The Society suggested that in addition to the courses already being given in some mining localitites, that Lancashire should be divided into two districts, corresponding with the Mining Inspection districts, and that a scientific and practical man be appointed to each division to give advanced lectures on mining subjects.

Henry Hall, 1904

In his Presidential Address to the Society in November, 1902, Henry Hall, an Inspector of Mines, warned of the penalties of ignoring industrial education. Germany, then one of Britain's main competitors in world markets, had always enforced education, and the attainment of certain standards exempted youths from a large part of their compulsory service in the army.

In arguments reminiscent of those still be voiced today, the theme of the necessity for increased technical education was to be made repeatedly to the Society over the next 15 years or so. "There is no doubt the average German schoolboy is far ahead of the average British schoolboy of the same age in respect of those subjects likely to be useful to him later in life," said Hall. Britain was making great efforts to establish technical and secondary schools and the large proportion of people who had to work for a living should "be taught with a book in one hand and a tool in the other."

A curriculum for one technical school included, amongst other practical subjects, mining, geology, steam engines, theoretical and applied mechanics, geometry, machine construction, metallurgy, textile studies, artistic and practical drawing, shorthand, typing, and hygiene nursing. The value of the work, said Hall, depended chiefly on the extent and character of the equipment of the various workrooms and laboratories. "Too much cannot be done in this direction, principles and theories are easily forgotten and in the absence of practice are quite valueless to the class in whose interests technical schools are being established," he went on.

To encourage children to take up technical education, incentives could be made, such as an increase in wages for those who successfully complete a course. The time was rapidly passing away, said Hall, when scholarly achievement was looked at with askance by employers who boasted that they were "practical men," because those employers were themselves being pushed into the background. With workmen willing to give a fair day's work for a fair day's pay, officered and directed by foremen having a thorough technical training, and the whole governed by men to "the manner born", and not necessarily the product of any system of education, Britain would not need to fear for the future of her industries.

John Burrows said the greatest qualifications a man could have for a job in the coal industry were a pair of strong arms and a good constitution, but the day was not far off when machinery would take over heavy work, and this would require skilled labour.

Advanced Mining Education, 1904

In September, 1904, George Winstanley, of the recently opened Department of Mining at the University of Manchester, gave the Society his views on the value of advanced mining education, which were based on the principles of practical experience. Mining studies, said Winstanley, had been neglected and coal was the last of the major industries to receive specialised attention. One problem facing both teachers and students was that mining covered a wide spread of disciplines, including geology, metallurgy, physics, mechanics, chemistry and mathematics.

"Not only is a knowledge of these matters essential, but one must be able to apply that knowledge usefully. At the same time, one must not lose sight of the fact that mining is an industry, and not a playground for experimental science," he went on. Collieries were not operated to give scope for "brains endowed more liberally with ingenuity than with common sense," and coal companies needed to be profit-making concerns providing livelihoods for 800,000 people. "Any system which loses sight of this fact entirely, fails in its object and becomes worse than useless." He did not think that lavish facilities were neccessary for studying mining, even at an advanced level, and the best laboratory was the working mine.

The three-year degree course at the University was run on a 'sandwich' basis. After a preliminary, or scientific year in college, the second and third years were divided between academic studies and work experience at local collieries. Students recommended by the University were articled, or made apprentices to mining engineering at nearby collieries, and in the second and third years of the course they spent at least two days each week at work. The University also ran a two-year diploma course for the mine manager's certificate.

Falling Behind

The First World War revealed how far Britain had fallen behind in technical education, particularly in the coal industry. Regrettably the Lancashire coalfield fared even well less than others in the provision of training, and Noah Williams, Honorary Secretary of the Society, drew attention to these serious shortcomings in a paper read in February,

1915. He pointed out that as early as 1845, a Government report had remarked on "the ignorance and inefficiency of many of the mine officials...and also the necessity...of a better system of general and technical education for miners."

A number of colliery disasters had lead to the Coal Mines Act of 1872 which required that managers should hold a certificate of competency, and this requirement was extended by the 1887 Act to under-managers. Training in theory and practice had been considered a necessity in other engineering industries, said Williams, but the feeling about the education of a colliery manager had been "As it was in the beginning, is now, and ever shall be." This outlook had not been beneficial and continental methods had had to be adopted in deep boring, sinking difficult shafts, washing, coking and the recovery of by-products.

Education was important to mine safety, but mining classes in the various coalfields had been aimed at ambitious miners and had not been of great service to the rank and file. "The miner in the dark recesses of the mine cannot be constantly supervised by the official," said Williams, "His work is of a perilous nature, and he is surrounded by dangers; his own life and that of others often depend upon his skill, intelligence, and knowledge." Williams suggested that a committee of educational authorities and mining men should arrange a series of lectures throughout the coalfield to discuss the daily dangers of work in the mines. The lectures would be of particular value to older miners, who could then encourage boys and younger men to attend voluntary evening classes.

Williams also drew attention to the great strain placed on young men attending night school several evenings a week after working all day. Neither did the British education system, where children could leave school at the age of 13, compare well with Germany, where elementary education was compulsory up to 14 years of age, followed by vocational daytime training up to the age of 18. With the prospect of mining becoming increasingly difficult, it was necessary for the country's good that managers should be well trained. Williams praised the establishment of the Wigan Mining College in 1857, but said that mining training in Lancashire in 1915 was not of the best. The only way a young miner could enter the ranks of management was by attending evening classes, but co-operation between the various educational bodies, employers and miners was very meagre.

For several years the Glamorgan and Monmouth County Councils had established technical instruction for mining students in the South Wales coalfield, and scholarships were available for students to go on to university, and to vist continental and British coalfields and engineering works. South Wales coalowners had also established two mining schools which provided a three year full-time mining course as well as part-time and special courses for colliery officials.

"In view of this magnificent movement in South Wales, it is obvious that Lancashire has much work to do in order to get into line with modern requirements," said Williams. He suggested that Manchester Geological and Mining Society could extend its sphere of influence by getting mining education extended and improved. Williams' paper drew a supportive response from both Society members and correspondents throughout the country who were involved in both the mining industry and education.

Familiar Theme

Just a year before the end of the First World War the topic of technical education and research was the keynote of the presidential speech of William Pickup. The theme was by now familiar, and Pickup claimed that despite improvements in mining education in other coalfields, no advances had been made in Lancashire.

"Hitherto mining engineers have generally trained in the pits. Theoretical knowledge has not been called for; it has even been held to be antagonistic to practical success. There has not been a supply of training mining engineers, partly because there has been no demand and partly because the places where a man could study the theoretical side of his profession were few and far between," he said.

The war had emphasised the deficiences of British technical training, but the days of unscientific mining were passing, and the industry of the future would be of greater complexity than in the past. Germany had built up her industries on the basis of experimental scientific investigation initiated in the universities and developed in the works. Britain's achievements in the chemical industry during three years of war had shown how great was the country's potential.

With the end of the war, another struggle of intense industrial competition would begin as nations attempted to recover lost markets and create new ones. "Unless we have the energy and enterprise to make ourselves fit and equipped for ...competition...we shall have a grievously heavy reckoning to pay for our national carelessness," forecast the President of the Society.

Pickup gave a detailed programme for the training of both men and management, which, so far as general education went, bore a striking resemblance to the German system. Boys should be transferred at the age of 12 from elementary schools to technical schools and begin work at 14 or 15. Up to the age of 18 there would be continuation school of four or six hours a week. Under-managers, surveyors, colliery mechanical and electrical engineers would be recruited from these ranks but would continue with their education at technical establishments. Inspectors of Mines, mining engineers, agents and general managers of large collieries would be trained at universities or technical colleges of university rank. Research too was of vital importance, and Pickup stressed the importance of close links between universities and industry.

Professor W. Boyd Dawkins commented that workmen in Britain had not yet had their fair share of the educational system, and it was absolutely neccessary to wake up from the Victorian state of apathy brought on by prosperity.

There was a sense of deja-vu almost 30 years later, when Dr R W Revans gave a lengthy paper to the society in February, 1947, on the education of under-officials. "Some of us may think enviously of our French and Polish colleagues. For in those countries, not to mention Germany, there are many established ways of training deputies and overmen that go far beyond anything we have ever dreamed of in Britain," he stated. "We have to take things as we find them, and they are not much different today from what they were in 1930 when the Holland Committee...advocated that ...the time had arrived to introduce a new type of deputy's examination of markedly higher standard. In a way I think it is a great pity that the recommendation was never carried out...for what is laid down as statutorily necessary is soon regarded as technically sufficient." Dr Revans went on to give a wide-ranging outline of the possibilities for improving education in mining, an area which was to improve considerably in the coming years.

A shortage of engineers did bring a training commitment from the newly-created National Coal Board, and talented young miners finishing apprenticeships were given the opportunity to study advanced engineering. Apart from university scholarships, young engineers were offered part-time courses, evening classes, refresher courses and full-time short courses.

In the years following nationalisation, education, the establishment of professional standards and examinations were a prime function of the Institution at national level, but the MGMS Branch played its own important role in the local activities of the Council of Engineering Institutions (CEI) and, later, the Engineering Council. In a presidential address in October, 1979, M.J.J.B. Owens looked at the future role of mining engineers, and, in part, the importance of education and training. "If the education system is to provide quality graduates for an industrial career with the intention of

120

ultimately improving engineering standards, a start must be made...when our youngsters are developing their characters." Owens urged that university and polytechnic education should be pursued and encouraged so that a pool of well-educated engineers would be available to meet the challenge of the future.

Manchester Geological and Mining Society Branch Council, 1987-88.
Back row, left to right: B. Chadwick, J. C. Fletcher, D. J. Henson, W. Mather, S. Hay, L. R. Boyfield, M. M. Danecke, C. Barber, D. Mort, W.
Swift, S. Gregory. Front row, left to right: J. Dearden, H. E. Tyson, G. W. Mapp, J. Hooton, W. Shawcross.

Members of Council not shown above:
G. Eaves, D. Hardman, W. E. Taylor, M. W. Brabbins, F. Jones, Dr. M. B. Jones, A. Purdy, A. Vincent and B. Carey.

CHAPTER TWELVE

Presidents of the Manchester Geological and Mining Society

1838-40	Lord Francis Egerton, MP
1841-43	James Heywood
1843-45	Sir Philip de Malpas Grey Egerton, MP
1845-57	Sir Oswald Mosley
1847-49	Ralph Thicknesse, MP
1849-51	James Heywood
1851-53	James Black
1853-55	G. W. Ormerod
1855-57	Sir Philip de Malpas Grey Egerton, MP
1857-59	E. W. Binney
1859-61	Sir James Kay-Shuttleworth, MP
1861-63	Joseph Dickinson
1863-65	Andrew Knowles
1866-67	E. W. Binney
1867-69	G. C. Greenwell
1869-71	John Aitken
1871-73	John Knowles
1873-74	Thomas Knowles
1874-75	Professor Sir William Boyd Dawkins
1875-76	Clifford R. Smith
1876-77	Professor Sir William Boyd Dawkins
1877-78	Joseph Dickinson
1878-79	John Edward Forbes
1879-80	The Earl of Crawford and Balcarres
1880-81	Sir Hugh J. Kay-Shuttleworth, MP
1881-82	George Gilroy
1882-83	John Aitken
1883-84	Edward Pilkington
1884-85	G. C. Greenwell
1885-86	Henry Mere Ormerod
1886-87	Professor Sir William Boyd Dawkins
1887-88	Joseph Dickinson

1888-89	John Knowles
1889-90	Sir Henry Hall
1890-91	John Burrows
1891-92	James Tonge
1892-93	Maskell William Peace
1893-94	William Scott
1894-95	William Watts
1895-96	Robert Winstanley
1896-97	Mark Stirrup
1897-98	John Ridyard
1899-1900	Sir William Scott-Barrett
1900-01	G. C. Greenwell
1901-02	J. Barnes
1902-03	Sir Henry Hall
1903-04	Col. G.H. Hollingworth
1904-05	John Gerrard
1905-06	Henry Bramhall
1906-07	Charles Pilkington
1907-08	John Ashworth
1908-09	Lt. Col. Sir Lees Knowles
1909-10	Sir William Garforth
1910-11	Alfred J. Tonge
1911-12	George B. Harrison
1912-14	Sir Thomas Holland
1914-16	Leonard R. Fletcher
1916-18	William Pickup
1918-20	A.J.A. Orchard
1920-21	Vincent Bramhall
1921-22	Sidney A. Smith
1922-23	Sir Thomas Ratcliffe-Ellis
1923-24	Clement Fletcher
1924-25	Professor Owen Thomas Jones
1925-27	Richard Landless
1927-29	H.O. Dixon
1929-31	James Gardiner
1931-33	Sir Harry Speakman
1933-34	F. Edmond
1934-36	W.J. Charlton
1936-37	J. Files
1937-39	Earl of Crawford and Balcarres
1939-41	F.S.W. Dobbs
1941-43	J.B. Sprostron
1943-44	T. Lund

1944-46	E.H. Frazer
1946-47	R.R. Ellis
1947-48	F.A. Ross
1948-49	D. Coatesworth
1949-51	F.G. Glossop
1951-52	J. Rutter
1952-53	G. Nicholls
1953-54	R. Hart
1954-55	James Anderton
1955-56	L.C. Timms
1956-57	R. Lowe
1957-58	H.E. Clegg
1958-60	J.C. Fletcher
1960-61	R. Foster
1961-62	G.W. Sanders
1962-64	E.J. Kimmins
1964-65	L.R. Boyfield
1965-66	H.E. Tyson
1966-67	W.J.W. Bourne
1967-68	G.J. Downend
1968-69	W. Bibby
1969-70	R. Barker
1970-71	K. Moses
1971-72	D. Grime
1972-73	S. Vardy
1973-74	J.G. Hind
1974-75	E. Hart
1975-76	W. Houldsworth
1976-77	C. Daniels
1977-78	W. Shawcross
1978-79	R.W.C. Blanshard
1979-80	M.J.J.B. Owens
1980-81	B. Dyer
1981-82	B. Carey
1982-83	A. Purdy
1983-84	D. Hardman
1984-85	R. J. Cole
1985-86	F. Jones
1986-87	G.W. Mapp

HONORARY MEMBERS IN 1987

James Anderton   W.J.W. Bourne   J. Bradshaw
E.J. Kimmins   H.E. Tyson

CHAPTER THIRTEEN

Milestones

It has been a difficult task to choose only four papers out of the many hundreds delivered to the Manchester Geological and Mining Society over the last 150 years. Three of the selected papers by distinguished members of the MGMS have a direct bearing on the Carboniferous coal measures, the source of greath wealth and industry. The fourth, on the Anderton Shearer Loader, is a tribute in particular to James Anderton, one of Lancashire's greatest mining engineers, and an acknowledgment in general of the contribution to the industry by mining engineers.

J. E. Bowman's paper was chosen to reflect the state of knowledge in 1840 of the still-young science of geology. For his discourse on The Origin of Coal, Bowman looked both to the traditional past and the beckoning era of rapid scientific growth. Binney's paper on Sigillaria of 1861 is an excellent example of the valuable work done in geological research by amateur, but diligent, workers. Dickinson's paper of 1905, on the Leading Features of the Lancashire Coalfield, was a modified version of a paper he first read to the Society 40 years earlier. Dickinson, a man of admirable practical ability, had a large knowledge of the coalfield, and his work in the coal industry was a tremendous force for good.

The 1955 paper on the Anderton Shearer Loader brings these selections from the Transactions up to modern times. Invented by a former president of the MGMS, the Shearer Loader pioneered the way for machines which have transformed the British coal industry.

On the Origin of Coal: and the Geological Conditions under which it was Produced

By J. E. Bowman, F.G.S., & F.L.S.
Read 30th January, 1840

To trace the operations of Nature in periods not only long anterior to all human records, but to the very creation of our species; to pronounce opinions respecting the structure of the globe on which we dwell during the progress of its formation, and of the successive changes necessary to fit it for the reception of organised and sentient beings, may appear at first to be presumptuous and beyond the reach of our limited and feeble powers.

But since it is the high and exclusive privilege of man to be endowed with observation and reflection, and feeling that it is a primary law of his nature, that in proportion to the active and legitimate employment of those faculties he becomes useful to others and happy in himself, it would indeed be strange if he could resist the impulse to exercise them on the grand and beautiful in nature which are every where so profusely scattered around him.

Such studies, far from being, as some timid minds have superficially supposed, hostile to Religion, are in fact, its best auxiliaries, by enlarging his conceptions of the Great Author of all things, and habitually leading him to refer every thing he sees to His power and benevolence. Nor when he scales the precipitous rock, or descends into the mine, will he fail to witness in the imbedded fossils, varous forms of organic life, now extinct, but which, in form, texture and general character, abundantly prove that the same great physical laws, the same harmony, and the same wisdom and design which still pervade and control universal nature, then existed.

These facts irresistibly lead him to penetrate in imagination, into those inconceivably remote epochs which his finite faculties can never fully estimate, and to trace in the mighty convulsions which then agitated its interior, the causes which have produced the existing conditions of the surface of our planet. To whatever geological formation he may direct his attention, he will not fail to be convinced that while all was yet without form and void, a Divine intelligence was controlling and modifying the elements, and preparing the earth to be fit receptacle for its future inhabitants.

While the successive orders of animated beings, however low in the scale of sentient existence, were endowed with an organisation best adapted to their several situations and wants, they were unconsciously contributing in varous ways, in life or after death, to bring about the designed end.

The luxuriant vegetables and forests that covered the primeval land seem to have had almost exclusively a prospective use; for they flourished in an atmosphere which, from its impurity no animal could probably have breathed, and long before intellectual man was introduced into this beautiful world to be charmed with their rich magnificence, and to wonder at their grotesque peculiar forms. Successive generations of these plants flourished and decayed without being of any apparent use; were sunk beneath the wastes and entombed under the bed of the ocean. They were slowly converted into Coal, and after a lapse of countless thousands of years, were again thrown, by other revolutions, upon or near the surface, and extracted by the intelligence and industry of man, to minister in so many ways, to his wants, his comforts, and his luxuries.

If we take into account that along with these precious beds of fossil fuel, are generally associated immense deposits of iron ore, which without the coal, would be to a great extent useless, I think we must admit that they collectively present one of the most striking instances of prospective design and benevolence excercised for the benefit of man at an incalculably remote period before he was called into existence.

The great commercial importance of fossil Coal, and the obscurity that, it must be confessed, still hangs over a portion of its history, have induced me to direct attention to some views which are probably new to many, and indeed are still far from being yet generally received by geologists themselves. The subject naturally divides itself into two distinct parts; the Origin of Coal: and the Geological Conditions under which it has been Produced.

As to the Origin of Coal.

Those whose recollections upon the subject extend back but a few years, are aware how little was then actually known, and how unsatisfactory were the conjectures as to the substance from which Coal was derived. But the experiments of Dr. MacCulloch following those of Hatchett and other previous investigators, have since so satisfactorily proved its vegetable origin, that I shall only need to touch briefly on this division of my subject.

In the ordinary process of vegetable putrefaction and destruction, a variety of compound gasses are formed by the reaction of their elements, and carbon alone, or rather carbon united to a portion of hydrogen, remains behind. The experiments just alluded to are in perfect harmony with this natural process, and have proved the following facts: That all vegetables, including wood, are chiefly composed of oxygen, hydrogen, and carbon: that in Peat, which is the first incipient stage of their decay produced by the action of water, the two latter elements form a hydro-carbonaceous compound, which communicates its brown colour to water: that peat itself does not appear to contain any bitumen, but that this latter substance in some of its modifications, as alphaltum, mineral tar, oil, or naphtha, is generated by the slow conversion and formation of the hydro-carbonaceous compound under pressure during which the complete separation of the hydrogen from carbon takes place, and the consolidation of the latter is completed; this however is a slow process, and a lengthened time is necessary to complete it. That bituminized wood, Surturbrand, Bovey Coal, etc as well as vegetables and Peat, contain hydrogen and carbon, and in greater proportion according to the degree of closeness and pressure to which they have been subjected under beds of soil, clay, etc.; that sufficient length of time being allowed, mere pressure and exclusion from the atmosphere are sufficient to convert bituminized peat and lignite into coal; and lastly, that the action of air and water on vegetable substances is similar to that of fire, though much slower and less complete.

Those who have paid attention to the formation of peat at the present day, are aware how closely in some of its more perfect states it approaches to coal; but as its different appearances may not be generally known, and will materially help us to understand how those vast depositories of fossil wealth were originally accumulated, a short notice of its growth and subsequent changes may be advantageously introduced.

A variety of our native plants,such as Mosses, Cottongrass, Rushes, Segs, Coarse Grasses, Ferns, Heather or Ling, etc., etc., chiefly natives of moist situations, enter into the composition of peat. In addition to the spongy texture of many of these, which enables them to arrest and retain the water around them, the mosses especially possess this peculiarity, as the root and lower extremity die and are decomposed, the part immediately beneath the surface, sends out fresh roots, the individual thus as it were becoming perennial, lengthening upwards, as the surface of the bog rises, while the lower and older portion decays, and furnishes a perpetual supply of decomposing vegetable matter.

A similar process takes place in the rushes and grasses, the original roots and lower leaves dying, while an annual renovation of both continues the existence of the plant upwards. This indeed is on their part but an effort of nature to excape being smothered by the thick and swelling beds of surrounding mosses, just as trees in a dense plantation shoot rapidly upwards, because their tops are the only part that light has access to, and loose their leaves and lower branches wherever that important element is excluded. In some Scotch peat bogs, Cottongrass (Eriophorum vaginatum) has been traced in an organized state to a depth of four feet beneath the surface, with numerous distinct tufts of roots one above the other, the lowest or oldest being in a state of the greatest decay, and the highest or last formed, alone ministering to the growth of the plant. In these the gradation downwards from the living vegetable to compact inorganic peat, is often easily traced. Above, where the living plant is in contact with the surface, the roots are fresh and healthy; lower down they are found vaccillating between life and death in a spongy half decomposed mass, and the pulverized carbonaceous matter is soon mixed with similar fibres still resisting decompsition. Proceeding downwards, these gradually disappear, till at length a black smooth semi-fluid substance alone is found, the process being completed by the total destruction of all the organised fibres.

In the deep peat bogs of the Hebrides, the lowest part is in this state of extreme decomposition, and its specific gravity is much greater than that of ordinary peat. When dried it burns with so bright a flame as to supercede the necessity of candles in the cottages of the poor, and with a glow of heat equal to that of the inferior kinds of coal; while it is capable of being formed into a compact charcoal fit for the purpose of the blacksmith. This peculiar structure of the plants and annual rise of the roots, naturally cause a very rapid increase in the thickness of the beds in which they grow. It is on record that some peat bogs in Scotland have been formed on fallen forests in the short space of fifty or sixty years: in Germany, cavities of seven feet deep have been filled with peat in thirty years. These however are extraordinary instances of rapidity beyond its usual rate of formation, which varies according to the humidity of the subsoil, the nature of the vegetation, and the warmth and moisture of the climate. It is important to bear these conditions in mind, because when we come to treat of the ancient vegetation which has formed the coal, it will naturally help us to comprehend, how, under the infinitely more favourable circumstances of a hotter climate and more humid atmosphere, those grotesque prototypes of our puny plants have acquired their gigantic dimensions - dimensions probably in many instances as much exceeding those of the plants now inhabiting the tropics, as the latter do the vegetables of an arctic climate.

It is well known that peat bogs such as those of our own island, are confined to temperate and cold latitudes, and that as we approach tropical regions, they become fewer and disappear altogether. From this circumstance an argument has been raised that Coal could not have originated from peat bogs, because at the time of its formation, the climate of this country was at least as hot as it now is between the tropics. This only holds with respect to the dissimilarity of the species, for as all plants, of whatever size and habit, are composed of the same elements: and as it is well known that their growth in the rank savannahs of the torrid zone is much more luxuriant and rapid than in cold countries, there is sufficient analogy to justify the comparison.

It is not contended that our peat bogs would ever produce solid coal, because no conditions in the present state of the earth's surface can ever resemble those of the carboniferous period as to climate and internal heat, and the submersion and pressure to which the ancient beds were subjected. Neither would the vegetation of a modern tropical forest; but the experiments of chemists show the gradual process of the bituminisation of decomposed vegetable matter, and that the more complete the process, the harder and more insoluble is the coal; while the great abundance of the fossil plants among the beds, and above all, the carbonisation of detached leaves in the shales and sandstones, incontestibly prove the general analogy and the vegetable origin of coal.

These views have now obtained the sanction of all competent observers: but there is still a reserve made with many, as to the origin of one species of Coal which is at present brought more prominently before the public, from its recent successful application to the navigation of steam vessels. I refer to the Stone Coal, Culm of South Wales, the Anthracite of mineralogists, which in its pure state does not occur in the Lancashire Coalfield, though some varieties may occasionally be found.

It has been rashly contended that it has not a vegetable basis, because no such remains have been found among it. This is by no means the case, portions of charcoal occur in the Anthracite of Pennsylvania, with its ligneous structure as well preserved as in recently prepared charcoal, and the circumstance of Anthracite being found in great quantities in the Great South Wales Coalfield, associated with the well known shales and sandstones, and consisting of almost pure carbon, leave no reasonable doubt upon the subject.

In Pembrokeshire the culm measures are distinctly seen reposing upon the Millstone Grit and carboniferous Limestone, occupying the precise geological position that the bituminous Coal does in the eastern part of the same basin, thus demonstrating that both were accumulated at the same period, and from the same material. In fact there is no coalfield in the world where the age of the deposit is more clearly marked by the natural sections, and Mr. Murchison says that plants common to other Coalfields occur not only in shales, but may be detected in the culm itself.

The Geological Conditions under which Coal has been Produced.

The great group of strata found in many districts in this country, and known by the general name of the Coal measures, consists of a indefinite number of beds of sandstones, shales, clays, and bituminous schists, repeatedly alternating with each other, generally containing Ironstone, and imbedding in no regular order of succession, thirty, or forty, or even sixty beds or seams of coal, each varying in thickness from a single inch to five or even ten yards.

This great formation succeeds and rests upon the Millstone Grit, which in its turn overlies the carboniferous, or Mountain Limestone. In Belgium, and the north of France, the southern parts of England, and northwards to the south of Yorkshire, and in Ireland, no Coal is found below the Millstone Grit; but as we advance further northwards we meet with beds interstratified with the latter formation, and even with the Mountain Limestone. The change first takes place a little to the north of Manchester, where at Gauxholme near Todmorden, two beds of coal are observed to lie within the Millstone Grit. But it is not my intention to enter much into the details of a coalfield which is much better known to most of my hearers than to myself, and as no general interest would be thereby excited, or elucidation afforded of the views I am about to explain, I shall satisfy myself with a few leading particulars of the most remarkable coalfields.

The greatest accumulation of coal in England is in the Wolverhampton and Dudley district,where there is one bed ten yards in thickness; the neighbourhood of Paisley presents ten beds whose united thickness is one hundred feet; while the great South Wales Coalfield contains, near Pontypool, twenty-three beds, containing altogether about ninety-three feet of solid coal. Professor Phillips says that generally the aggregate thickness of all the beds of coal in a district is about fifty feet; but this uniformity does not apply to the accompanying shales and grits, which vary very much in this respect.

Various theories have been framed to account for the production of this enormous thickness of deposits, and especially of the seams of Coal. Some have supposed they have been formed and accumulated from Algae at the bottom of the sea, or from plants drifted from tropical climates: or in lakes and estuaries from plants brought into them from neighbouring lands, first held in suspension and then precipitated to the bottom; while others have recourse to a series of reciprocating inundations of salt and fresh water, and of elevations and subsidences of the bottom, which sound geology cannot sanction.

Mr. De La Beche says, "By general consent, Coal has been considered as resulting from the distribution of a body of vegetable remains upon previously deposited surface of sand, argillaceous silt or mud, now compressed into shales and sandstones. After the distribution of the vegetables, other sands, silts or mud, were accumulated upon them; and this kind of operation was continued irregularly for a considerable time, during which there was an abundant growth of similar vegetables at no very distant place, to be suddenly, at least in part, destroyed and distributed over considerable areas on the more common detritus.

Great length of time would be requisite for this accumulation, because the phoemomena observed would lead us to consider the transporting power, though variable, to have been generally moderate: moreover a very considerable growth of vegetables requiring time, would be necessary at distinct intervals: for coal beds now only six or ten feet thick, must, before pressure was exerted upon them, have occupied a much greater depth." This is a pretty correct statement of the prevailing views as to the mode of formation of beds of Coal at the bottom of lakes and esturaries, but some parts of the supposed process, as it appears to me, could never take place. It is not denied that some plants might be drifted from neighbouring or even distant lands; on the contrary, this was problably the case in many instances, to some extent; indeed it is rendered almost certain from the occurrence of detached leaves and branches of fern and other plants in most of the alternating shales and sandstones. Such drifted materials would be arrested by shoals, and lodged in hollows or estuaries, or entangled among the mud during its precipitation and consolidation.

But there is difficulty in conceiving how the vast masses of vegetable matter necessary to form a thick seam of Coal, being so much lighter than water, could be made to sink and be kept down at the bottom, while a sediment, heavier than themselves, was in the act of being deposited upon them, instead of sinking through and underneath them, as is natural to expect it would do. This difficulty is increased, when we reflect that without a super-incumbent layer of mud or sand to give the requisite confinement and pressure, the process of conversion into coal could not go on; for the bituminous matter, and especially the hydrogen, would, from their less specific gravity

134

immediately rise to the surface as they were formed, and be dissipated, and consequently ordinary coal could not be formed. Besides, this supposed distribution of a body of vegetable matter upon a previously deposited surface of sand or mud, could not have been made so uniformly over such areas as the beds of coal cover, if it had been drifted by currents; for the natural operation of such currents would be to accumulate it irregularly on either side, while the actual courses of the currents would by their erosive action, be destitute of any portion.

In general, the coal-beds, with some modifications, may be traced over very considerable areas; the Lower Main Seam of the Great Northern Coalfield is known to extend over an area of at least two hundred square miles, and is problably continued over double or treble that space: and in our Lancashire series, Mr. E. W. Binney informs me there is a thin coal seldom exceeding a foot, or being less than eight inches, and lying below the Gannister or Rabbit Coal, which extends all the way from Whaley Bridge to Blackburn.

There is no trace of currents or violent action of water in the coal formation. The fine silts and mud, now converted into shales, bind, clunch, etc., are evidences of the most tranquil state of the water from which they were precipitated, and such a thing as a rolled pebble imbedded in these strata or in the coal itself, is rarely seen. These facts seems to indicate that the beds were actually deposited in gulfs or inland sea, where the tides and currents of the ocean were either entirely absent, or exerted but a feeble action. The existing situation of the Gulf of Mexico, into which large rivers pour their tributary waters, offers so many coincidences to what may be supposed took place during the carboniferous period, that a slight reference thereto may help us to form a tolerable idea how the shales and sandstones of the coal formation were deposited, and from whence the materials were derived.

Here is an immense area of water extending over eighteen degrees of latitude, and thirteen degrees of longitude, receiving the contributions of numerous great rivers, expecially from the north and west: these rivers traverse countries situated in widely different latitudes and climates, and composed of various geological formations. One of these rivers, the Mississippi, will serve to illustrate our present subject: and without going much into detail, we may say that it is four thousand miles long, and is the drainage of an immense region stretching from the Alleghenys on the east, to the Rocky Mountains on the west, and eleven times the area of Great Britain and Ireland.

Its tributaries are mighty rivers, and the delta formed at its mouth by the sedimentary mud which its waters bring down, is two hundred miles long, and one hundred broad, and is composed of distinct strata

135

varying considerably in colour and specific gravity. The great difference in latitude, and the various mountain chains which head these rivers, their greater or less elevations, and consequently the different months in which the sun can act upon the snows and ices on their slopes, and of the plains in the higher parts of their course, will necessarily cause the floods and freshes to take place in different parts of the summer: and the thick yellow mud of the Missouri, the red clay of the Arkansas and Red River, and the blue and black sediment of some of the other tributaries will be separately discharged into the Gulf, without being mixed up together in the great trough of the Mississippi. Thus the sections of the delta which have been cut through by the shifting of the channels, show various alternations of red, black, and blue clays, and sands and muds more or less micaceous, of finer or coarser texture, according to the chemical or mechanical conditions of the formation from which they have been severally derived.

The analogy is greater between these deposits,and shales of the carboniferous era, owing to the slight fall of the waters, allowing the finer particles to reach the delta, while the gravel and pebbles would be left behind near the mouths of tributaries, where they enter the central valley. Nor are these different sedimentary deposits for the most part carried out by the gulfstream, for hydrographers inform us that a current is scarcely perceived eastward of the Mississippi, the waters there, and even as far south as the reefs of Florida, and to the Bahama Islands, being among the clearest of the sea-waters yet discovered. The bulk, therefore, of the immense volume of sedimentary mud brought down by the Mississippi, and also by the numerous other rivers that discharge themselves into it, must accumulate at the bottom of the gulf.

Nor should it be hastily concluded that the analogy will not hold, because we see at present near the great coal basins of England, no extensive surrounding continents at all adequate to justify the inference that they could have supplied that enormous mass of sedimentary shales and sandstones which compose the coal measures. It is the very extent of this accumulation which may help us to a solution of the difficulty.

Geological observations everywhere show that the relative position of land and water is constantly undergoing changes; it can be demonstrated that our present continents have been once the bed of the ocean, and that even at the time when the coal strata were in progress of formation, a large portion of the present continent of Europe was under the sea. If then, we find, as we do among the great northern drift, boulders which we cannot refer to any existing mountains, may it not be supposed that the lands and mountains from which the coalshales were derived, may been since entirely swept

136

away, and their places now occupied by the ocean? The vast length of time necessary for effecting such extensive changes, cannot be considered a valid objection; for the Geologist soon becomes convinced that immense periods have doubtless been required for the completion of all operations effected by the agency of sedimentary deposits.

The above reference to the sedimentary deposits of the Mississippi is more or less applicable to all large rivers, and, is only intended to show how the shales and sandstones of the coal measures may have been accumulated. I shall now proceed to consider the geological circumstances which have produced the intermediate beds or seams of Coal.

The permancy and stability of mountain chains and of the land in general, and the fluctuation of the level of the ocean, used to be, and perhaps still is, except among geologists, the prevailing belief: but the concurrent testimony of all accurate observation of the changes still taking place in the relative levels of land and sea, prove that the converse is the fact, namely, that the general level of the ocean is fixed and permanent, and has never much varied from what it is at present: but that the land on every part of the globe is frequently undergoing changes from a lower to a higher level, or from a higher to a lower.

In the former case, the bed of the ocean was first thrown up into mountain chains, which appeared above the surface as rocky islands, and then by a repetition of the elevatory causes, the surrounding parts appeared as plains and valleys, constituting together a continent. In the latter case, namely, during a period of subsidence, the valleys and plains first became submerged, leaving the mountains as insulated chains, or completely burying them beneath the waves. So many well authenticated instances of these subsidences and elevations are on record in the works of geologists, and have been collected by the industry of Mr. Lyell, and more recently by Mr. Darwin, that it is merely necessary to mention a few of the most striking.

During the earthquake of Cutch in the delta of the Indus, in Bombay, in 1819, a tract of country upwards of thirty miles in length was converted from dry land into sea in the course of a few hours, but so uniformly that the four towers of the Fort of Sindree continued standing, so that the people within who had ascended to the top saved themselves in boats. Immediately after the shock, at the distance of five miles, rose a long elevated mound, where there had been a low and perfectly level plain. This newly raised country was upwards of fity miles in length, and its breadth about sixteen miles.

In one geological epoch and district, a series of elevations may be taking place by slight and repeated paroxysmal efforts of subterranean gases at escape, as has long been and still is taking place on the west coast of South America, the shores of the Baltic, and many other places; while on the contrary, a subsidence from the settling of the earth's crust, may either simultaneously, or in another epoch, be going on in a different portion of the surface.

In 1692 Jamaica was visited by a dreadful earthquake, and many parts of the coast, with houses, etc., were sunk thirty to forty feet beneath the waves. In 1755, the Quay at Lisbon sank at once to a depth of six hundred feet. A celebrated French geologist, Elie de Beaumont, supposes that in the history of the earth there has been long periods of comparative repose, during which the deposition of sedimentary matter has gone on with regular continuity: and that there have also been short periods of paroxysmal violence, during which the continuity was broken. Mr. Darwin has shown that in the Pacific, an extent of ocean more than one thousand miles in one direction, and several hundreds in another, is scattered over with islands which are now in a course of very gradual subsidence from the action of subterranean causes. While on the South American continent, elevations are taking place over wide areas with a very uniform force, proofs of which appear in terraces of stones and shells found in the high valleys of the flanks of the Andes. These changes of level are now so well understood, that it would be a waste of time to enter into further details: the general fact is completely established.

The changes which seem principally to have been in operation during the formation of the Coal measures, were subsidencies of the land; and I shall consider these subsidencies as the basis of what has long appeared to me the most satisfactory and consistent explanation of the facts observed as to the superposition of the beds of coal, and their irregularities in distance from each other, in thickness, and in continuity. It seems to be the only theory which has the advantage of being in accordance with the recognized laws of nature now in operation: and requires none of those accommodating alternations of elevations and subsidencies which have now been called in aid by some geologists, but which are required to be too numerous and too regular to merit the sanction of the independent observer.

The theory I am about to propose is not altogether new: and in a somewhat modified form has been held by many eminent geologists. Jameson long ago considered that the plants from which coal was formed, once stood and grew in the places where they are buried. Brongniart thought it was probable that the beds were formed from vegetables, which after their death passed into a kind of peaty deposits of greater or less extent, on which other vegetables still grew, till, as DeLuc imagined, they afterwards slipped into the sea, or by other

138

means, became covered by beds of rocks, and there gave rise to the Coal deposits.

If, for this awkward mode of entombment in the waters, we substitute a submergence of the land when covered by the vegetable mass, I think we shall not be far from the truth. The authors of the Fossil Flora after adverting to various circumstances, arrive at the conclusion that the beds of Coal chiefly originated in vegetable matter which lived, died, and was decomposed upon the spots where we now find it; each bed having been the product of an extended surface of marshy land, covered with a rank luxuriant vegetation.

These views have been recently advocated in a Paper, read by Mr. T. B. Beaumont before the London Geological Society, and are in unison with my own. My opinion is simply this - That the trees and vegetables from which the beds of Coal are derived, grew on the identical spots the latter now occupy, when each bed was successively the surface, and probably was but little raised above the level of the waters, either as detached islands or extensive plains or savannahs; that these surfaces, during the settling of the earth's crust, were one after another submerged and covered with sediments from turbid waters, or with drifted clay, sand, and shells which buried up the plants: that these sedimentary deposits gradually accumulated till they formed a new surface, which in time produced another growth of plants and trees, and after a second period of rest, were in their turn submerged and covered up by other deposits: and that similar intervals of repose with intermittent occasional subsidencies, were repeated during the entire period of the Coal formation. As each vegetable surface sunk beneath the waters, it gradually became converted into Coal by processes already explained, and the successive deposits of mud and sand became consolidated into shales and sandstones.

The enormous aggregate depth of the whole coal formation, and the great thickness of some of the beds of shale, etc., incontestibly prove the long periods that must have been required to complete them. This slow deposition is in harmony with what we observe in all other geological epochs, and has kept going on till the accumulated sediment has formed a shoal, which has gradually reached the surface, by degrees has resisted the encroachment of the waters, and then established itself as an island. As the channels between the different islands became choked up with sediment, marshy plains or morasses would be formed, and would unite the islands into plains, upon which vegetation would soon commence, and favoured by great heat and moisture, would rapidly prepare a soil for the growth of the larger succulent plants, and for forests of hardwood trees and coniferoe.

All this, however, implies a long interval of rest; for however rapidly the lofty soft and spongy Lepidodendrons and creeping Stigmarias would develop themselves in moist atmosphere and uniformly high temperature, many generations of them must have been necessary to supply a sufficient quantity of vegetable mould for the forest trees, and of carbonaceous matter for the thicker beds of Coal, reduced as they are in bulk, by subsequent superincumbent pressure. The Fossil Trees which were lately discovered in our own neighbourhood, on the line of the Bolton Railway, and which will form the subject of a separate paper, throw out roots as thick as those of an oak two hundred years old, and must have required a long period for their growth. Centuries of rest have probably elapsed during the accumulation of those vegetable masses in which the thicker seams of Coal have originated: while the extreme thinness of other, proves that the paroxysms have taken place at irregular intervals, and have sometimes succeeded each other rapidly.

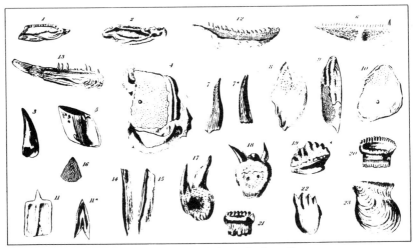

Fossils from Dixon Fold drawn by Capt. Brown

There is a peculiarity in the texture of Coal, which has not received the attention it deserves. If it be closely examined, it will be found to consist of a series of parallel horizonatal laminae, varying in thickness from the fourth to the sixteenth of an inch, often adhering closely together, but sometimes with an intermediate layer of fibrous glossy charcoal, in broken portions, which causes it to separate easily.

These laminae are best observed in the cross fracture and often exhibit considerable difference in compactness and lustre, some being so much more bituminous and shining than others, that they may be traced for a great length. This structure, though in some coal seams indistinct, is so general, that it seems to point to some law which the chemical geologist might advantageously investigate. Does the Coal of some of these laminae differ in the proportions of its carbon, hydrogen, and oxygen, from others above or below it? Has that which contains more hydrogen, because formed from resinous vegetables, (the conifererae), separated and arranged itself above others while in the fluid state, because its specific gravity was less. Does this laminar structure indicate that each thin layer, as it became bituminized, has been separately converted into Coal by a process commencing at the bottom of the mass, and proceeding gradually upwards? Or, lastly, can it be reconciled with the idea of the simultaneous consolidation of the whole bed?

There is another feature in every Coal Field, familiar to all connected with the working of the mines; I allude to the inequality in the thickness of some of the seams. This may be accounted for by the irregularity of the subsidence over extended areas, and may result from the greater or less distance of different parts of the vegetable surface from the axis of convulsion. The disturbances would act with various intensity upon a plain or morass, extending over fifty or one hundred square miles, elevating some portions, perhaps, and depressing others below the level of the waters. We will suppose such a movement as this to take place after a long period of rest, during which a thick stratum of vegetable matter had been accumulating, which had hitherto preserved a pretty uniform thickness. What will be the result? The progress of vegetation immediately ceases upon those portions which have been submerged, and they are soon coverd with a deposition of mud, sand, or silt, which, if no second submersion take place, will continue to accumulate till it reaches the surface of the water.

Vegetation will then commence upon it, and will go on simultaneously with that on the contiguous land, where, during this interval, not having been submersed, it has been going on uninteruptedly, and increasing the thickness of the bed. At length another and more general subsidence takes place: the whole area of the plain is sunk beneath the waters, is gradually buried under a series of muddy sediments, and by time and pressure is ultimately converted into Coal.

It will easily be comprehended how these partial subsidences might be modified by local circumstances, so as to produce that variety in the thickness of the beds, which is often found in in different parts of the same Coal Field: as well as to account for the occasional thinning out of the coal seams, and for the interposition of shale, clay, or sandstone in thin beds, or scattered patches with the Coal. A bed of

141

Coal formed from the vegetation of an insulated tract, would necessarily be limited to a corresponding shape and extent: but other neighbouring lands would also be covered with vegetation: and it is easy to understand that a seam of Coal formed from the whole by a general subsidence, would be distinguished by some discrepancies and interruptions of continuity.

We may thus account for those partial irregularities which occur, amidst a general uniformity in all extensive Coal Fields.

The subsidences of which I have been speaking, must not be confounded with those more violent convulsions which took place after the consolidation of the beds, and subsequently to the carboniferous era: which broke up whole districts in every direction, elevating some portions, and depressing others, and produced those extensive dislocations generally known by the name of Faults.

In conclusion, I have not adverted to the question that has been often asked, whether the water that prevailed at the period of the coal formation were salt or fresh, because it does not affect the views I have endeavoured to explain, as to the formation of Coal. It is probable that both salt and fresh water were present at different periods, and in different portions of the field: for while the corals and shells of the intermediate Limestones in the Newcastle district, and the Pectens and Goniatites of the lower measures in the Lancashire and Yorkshire, indicate marine conditions, the Unios and Cypris of the upper measures are equally strong in favour of a fresh water origin.

Editor's note: References to various drawings etc., have been omitted.

ON SIGILLARIA AND ITS ROOTS

by E. W. Binney, F.R.S., F.G.S.
A paper read in May, 1861

N o part of geology has excited more attention than the study of the valuable coal-fields of England, which have been explored with superior care to any other portion of the earth's surface of similar extent.

Whether we view them as the grand herbaria of the ancient world, or consider them as the sources of our national greatness, they are alike worthy of attention. On the present occasion an attempt will be made to bring before your notice some of the extraordinary forms of the vegetable kingdom that, countless ages ago, flourished upon the surface of that part of the globe now constituting our coal-fields.

But before doing this it will be proper to present you with a general sketch of the chief advantages which England has derived from that most valuable of mineral products, coal. It is to this that we owe our vast manufacturing districts and the numerous population to which they afford subsistence. Coal, as a fuel, not only saves from the woodman's axe the beautiful timber trees that adorn our rural scenery, and which in other less favoured countries are consigned to the flames for the purpose of yielding heat, but it supplies us with the giant power of steam, that unceasingly works our unrivalled machinery, enables us to annihilate distance on the railway, and, in despite of wind and tide, drives our noble steamers across the trackless ocean.

In the hands of the chemist, coal supplies us with the brilliant gas that dispels the darkness from our streets: it gives the colouring matter of the gorgeous pinks, blues and greens of the calico printer: it supplies pitch and tar for the preservation of our timber: naptha as a solvent for india-rubber, in the formation of our waterproof fabrics: oils as substitute for vegetable and animal oils for the purpose of lubricating machinery and burning in lamps; paraffin as a wax for candles, and the various salts of ammonia used in calico printing and other departments of the arts.

Latterly alcohol has been obtained from coal: whilst from coal-tar, a substance having the medical properties of quinine, as well as being a valuable dye, and also essential oils resembling those obtained from lemons, almonds, pears, etc., and used in scenting soaps and flavouring confectionery, have been extracted. All these last-named useful products are obtained from coal in the manufacture of gas, and were, until lately, thrown away as refuse, and the gas producer had hard work to dispose of them, unless he could turn them into an old abandoned coal-pit.

Strictly speaking, coal cannot be termed a mineral, for it is not composed of inorganic matter. It is vegetable matter chemically changed, and more or less mixed with mineral matter. The bright part of coal, which does not soil the fingers on being touched, shows no more trace of structure than pitch, but the pulverulent, carbonaceous matter, so frequently found in coals, which soils the fingers, is nothing more than charcoal, and, like charcoal, it contains abundant traces of structure.

If you were to boil a piece of pitch until it became fluid, and then mix it with crushed charcoal, this mass, on cooling, would show something of the appearance that coal does, the bright part exhibiting no structure, whilst the dull part, or charcoal, would shew (sic) the vessels of the wood from which the charcoal was produced.

Time will not permit an exhibition or description of the many delicate plants which abound in the roofs of our coal-mines, and even if they did, these specimens, being generally but detached leaves and stems, would give but little information. They might have been drifted by currents of water to the places where they are not found, or they might have grown there. No positive evidence can be adduced in support of either hypothesis.

The case is very different, however, with regard to some of the larger plants found in the coal measures, and it is to two of them best known to the public,namely, those hitherto classed under the genera stigmaria, and sigillaria, that your attention will now be directed. Both these plants are undoubtedly found upon the places where they once grew and flourished, and scarcely a seam of coal, when rigidly examined, is destitute of some traces of them.

On Stigmaria

First, then, with regard to the Stigmaria. Probably no fossil plant has excited more discussion among botanists than the stigmaria, about which, although the commonest in the whole number of plants found in the coal-measures, there was till lately the greatest uncertainty as to its real nature. In the Lancashire coalfield traces of it can be found in

144

every mine. It abounds in all the floors of the coals generally unmixed with any other plants, and having stringy fibrels formerly considered as leaves, but now proved to be rootlets, radiating from the stem in all directions, and often the rootlets alone are seen without the stem.

By careful observation it is also to found in the upper and lower portions of most of the seams of coal, often with its stringy appendages. (It has often been stated that stigmaria is only found in coal floors. It is not so: for sigillariae, lepidodendra, calamites, and other common coalplants are often met with in the roofs of coal-seams and in the upper parts of the beds of the coal. This is fully stated by me in a paper read before the British Association, at the Manchester meeting, in 1842. Of all plants they have contributed most to the formation of coal. In the examination of their structure not only will great light be thrown on physiological botany, but much valuable information will be afforded as to the origin of coal.) It is also more rarely met with in the roofs of coalmines, and in sandstone rocks. The specimens in the floors are the most numerous, and they are generally found to strike down from the lower part of the coal into the clay underneath; sometimes, when this deposit is a thick one, at a considerable angle, and when it is thin, nearly horizontal.

Among the many authors who have written on this plant, probably no one has shown so accurate a knowledge of it as Mr. Steinhaur. In an elaborate paper printed in the first volume of the new series of the American Philosophical Transactions he describes the most perfect form of the fossil as that of a cylinder, more or less compressed, and generally flatter on one side that the other. Not unfrequently the flattened side turns in so as to form a groove. The surface is marked in quincuncial order, with pustules, or rather depressed areolae, with a rising in the middle, in the centre of which rising a minute speck is often observable. From different modes and degrees of compression, and probably from different states of the original vegetable, these areolae assume very diffent appearances; sometimes presenting indistinct rimae, like the bark of an aged willow: sometimes, as in the shale impressions, exhibiting little more than a neat sketch of the concentric circles.

He was of opinion that the fibrous processes, acini, spines, or whatever else they might be called, were cylindrical, that small fragments of these cylinders showed distinctly a central line of pith, coinciding with the point in the centre of the pustule, and that some of these extended to the length of 20 feet. He also notices the groove of the cylinder being always under, and suggests that the pith has fallen down from the centre: and after further details he concludes "that the stem was a cylindrical stem or root, growing in a direction nearly horizontal in the soft mud at the bottom of fresh water lakes, or seas, without branches, but sending out fibres from all sides. That it was furnished in the centre with a pith of a structure different from the surrounding wood or cellular substance, more dense and distinct at the older end of the plant, and more similar to the external substance towards the termination which continued to shoot. And perhaps that besides this central pith there were longitudinal fibres proceeding through the plant like those of the roots of pteris auilla. With respect to any stem arising from its, if a creeping trunk, we have hardly ground for a supposition."

Messrs. Lindley and Hutton, after noticing at great length Steinhaur's remarks in volume 1 of their Fossil Flora, come to the following conclusions:

1. That it was a prostrate land plant, the branches of which radiated regularly from a common centre, and finally became forked.
2. That it was succulent plant.
3. That it was a dicotyledonous plant.
4. That the tubercles on the stem are the places from which the leaves have fallen.
5. That the leaves were succulent and cylindrical.

These authors in their introductory chapter of the second volume of their work, after stating that they had two perfect specimens , found in the roof of the Bensham seam of the Jarrow Colliery, state "that the centre of the plant was a continous homogeneous cup, or dome, and not the remains of the arms squeezed into a single mass, as they before had supposed, a land plant,but that it grew in soft mud, most likely of still and shallow water, as they had found its remains associated with an undescribed species of Unio.

On Sigillaria

None of the vegetable forms constituting the flora of the carboniferous epoch have excited more attention, as it regards their general character, than those which are included in the genus sigillaria.

They are extremely abundant in the great coal formations of the British island, and are found in a similar and probably contemporaneous deposits on the continent and in North America. In some instances they appear to have attained a considerable size. M.Adolphe Brongniart mentions a specimen discoverd in one of the coal-mines of Kunzwerk, near Essen, in Westphalia, measuring full forty feet in length. I have seen some full that height, while others do not appear to have exceeded ten feet in an advanced stage of their growth.

The genus sigillaria may be readily distinguished by the stems of its various species being externally marked with a number of longitudinal furrows, and by each of the raised spaces or ribs between the furrows having a single row of scars, in some cases nearly in contact, and in others considerably apart.

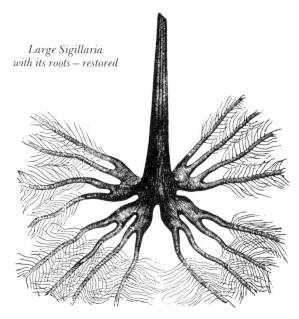

*Large Sigillaria
with its roots – restored*

Various opinions have been entertained respecting the position of sigillaria in the vegetable kingdom. Schlotheim supposed it to be allied to the palms; Von Martius to the cactuses and the euphorbias: Brongniart to the tree ferns: while Lindley and Hutton, as stated in the "Fossil Flora," appear to agree with Von Martius, but do not give any decided opinion on the matter. A few years have now elapsed since these opinions were advanced.

The discovery, however, of a silicified specimen of this plant at Autun, exhibiting its constituent tissues in a nearly complete state, induced Brongniart, the only author who has since written on the subject, entirely to change his opinion. (Archives du Museum d'Histoire Naturelle. In this valuable paper, on sigillaria elegans the learned author fairly states the reasons for and objections against stigmaria being the root of sigillaria.) At the present time we may safely assume that little has been published as to the structure and nature of the large specimens of sigillaria met with in our coal-fields.

In the year 1839, in company with Rev. Robert Wallace and Mr. Atkinson, F.G.S., I examined some upright specimens of the stems of sigillaria reniformis, which were found resting upon a small seam of coal exposed in cutting the tunnel at Clay Cross, on the North Midland Railway, near Chesterfield. I distinctly traced a stigmaria to the lower part of a sigillaria. Not being able certainly to prove the absolute insertion of one plant into the other, it could not be positively affirmed that they were portions of the same plant, but a full conviction was arrived at that Messrs. Lindley and Hutton had been mistaken in supposing that the stigmaria was a domed or a cup-shaped plant, and that it had no upright stem.

Accordingly, in a paper, read in 1840, on the fossil fishes of the Pendleton coal-field I stated that the stigmaria grew in water, on rich mud, in a bay, like the mangrove of the tropics, at the mouth of the Niger, in the Brass country. For several years after I examined a great number of upright sigillaria for the express purpose of acquiring a correct knowledge of their roots.

Many practical colliers having seen upright stems of sigillaria with their roots resting a small seams of coal only 8 to 12 inches in thickness, the floors of which were full of root-like stigmaria, very naturally concluded that the latter were the roots of the former. M.Adolphe Brongniart announced that perhaps stigmaria was the root of the sigillaria, from the great similarity in their internal structure. Professor Wm King, of Galway, and other geologists have also made similar statements, but their opinion received little consideration, owing to their not being able to bring any facts in support of it.

The first specimens of fossil trees that distinctly proved that stigmaria was only the root of sigillaria were three discovered in Mr. Littler's stone quarry at Scotch Row, St Helens, in the early part of 1843. I first saw them on the 9th of August in that year. At the meeting of the British Association, at Cork, I announced to the geological section there the fact of stigmaria being the root of sigillaria, but no one heeded or believed it, except Sir Charles Lyell, who was at once struck with the importance of the discovery.

The late respected Dean of Westminster also immediately threw away his own ideas as to the nature of the plant described in the Bridgwater Treatise, on hearing the above observations on the St. Helens specimens.

On 28th of October, 1848, I read a description of the trees before the Manchester Geological Society, and Mr. J.F. Bateman, F.G.S., was about the only person who supported the views put forward. His opinion on the matter was certainly of greater value than those of the gentlemen who held a contrary opinion, as none of them had then seen the specimens just alluded to, but had gathered their information from books describing different specimens. That paper was published in the

Philosophical Magazine for March, 1844.

For some time after its publication, owing to the quarry, where the specimens were, not being much worked, they remained unnoticed, until Professor Harkness, F.R.G., and myself uncovered and exposed the large specimen. An account of this specimen appeared in the Philosophical Magazine for October, 1845. Certainly since that time no more conclusive evidence has appeared to prove that stigmaria was the root of sigillaria. The singular regularity of the roots and their bifurcations - that sigillaria were found in situ, midway between seams of coals - points clearly and decisively proved beyond question by the St. Helen's trees.

In the proceedings of the Geological Society for 1846 is an account by me of the sigillaria found at Dukinfield by Messrs. Swire & Lees, and liberally presented by those gentlemen to the Museum of the Manchester Geological Society. That communication was read on the 22nd April, in the year just named. The specimen, thanks to Messrs. Swire and Co., was got out of the floor of the mine at great trouble and expense, and placed in the Museum of our Society, where the public can see it. This root is without doubt the most valuable and interesting fossil vegetable that is to be met in any Museum in the world. The tree did not afford real information beyond what I had obtained from the St. Helen's trees, but it confirmed in my opinion in every particular, especially in that of the main roots of large specimens possessing none of the characters of stigmaria.

In a paper read before the Literary and Philosophical Society of Manchester on 6th July, 1847, I described a goodly number of sigillaria discovered by me in the Pemberton Hill cutting, on the Bury and Liverpool Railway. (My friend Dr. J.D. Hooker, F.R.G., visited these specimens with me. I owe much to him for assisting me to make the scientific public believe the facts that I had seen and published. Without his kind aid it would have been difficult to do even that.) It is there distinctly stated that all the upright trees (sigillaria reniformis) had roots of stigmaria with their rootlets traversing the silty clay in all directions.

In a communication to the Geological Society of London, read on the 2nd May, 1849, I described the occurrence of spores in the inside of casts of stigmaria, and noticed the remarkable crucial sutures found under the base of the stems of sigillaria. In a paper printed in the Quarterly Journal of the Geological Society for 1858, information is given as to the origin of the medulary rays and the nature of the vascular bundles in the pith of stigmara, as well as the structure of the rootlets of the same plant.

It seems right to put on record a distinct and connected statement of the steps which led to the discovery of the relation that stigmaria bears to sigillaria, as well as to give a circumstantial account of the specimens by means of which that discovery was effected, since the value of these specimens, for the purpose for which they were used, is still liable to be underated, and, consequently, the completeness of the discovery, to which they so effectually contribute, is sometimes called in question. For, in a work published in 1854, in Edinburgh, on Arcadian Geology, by John William Dawson, F.G.S., and which has only lately come under my notice, that gentleman, in alluding to Mr. Brown's discoveries on sigillaria, states - "Mr. Binney can claim priority in date of publication, but his specimens were much less perfect in details of structure, and therefore less satisfactory than those described by Mr. Brown."

Though I have not seen these specimens, yet, from what Mr. Brown says of them, and from Sir Charles Lyell's engraving it appears, not that stigmaria is the root of sigillaria, but the root of lepidodendron: and it seems that in Mr. Brown's paper on the fossil, in the Quarterly Journal of the Geological Society for 1847, he describes it as a lepidodendron.

From the drawing of the specimen, it is almost impossible to make anything out in regard to the genus it belongs to, except that its stem and roots are covered with numerous dots. The only thing it proves is that stigmaria is a root, which, at that time, was pretty well known in England, however new it might be considered in America. Aged sigillarieae, when decorticated, present on the surface of the lower parts of their stems and main roots a gnarled and ruggedly striated appearance, like an old oak, a peculiarity noticed by my friend Mr. Bowman, in his description of the Dixon Fold trees.

In the Dukinfield specimen, with its four main roots bifurcating into 8 secondary and then into 16 tertiary roots, no trace of the areolae of stigmaria can be seen in any of the main, the secondary, or the beginning of the tertiary ones; they are only seen when the latter assume the thickness of ordinary stigmaria at some six feet from the base of the stem.

My specimens, here mentioned, prove beyond doubt that stigmaria is the root of sigillaria. It will probably be found that this character of root was common to several other genera of aquatic plants besides sigillaria, but this point yet requires to be carefully examined and proved. In the annexed woodcut I give a representation of a restored large sigillaria, with its full complement of 16 tertiary roots its cylindrical stem, but I have not ventured to crown it with a magnificent frond of fern leaves as my friend Mr. B. Waterhouse Hawkins, F.G.S., has done in a beautiful small drawing which he has presented to me.

Nearly every part can be proved by the Dukinfield specimen previously alluded to.

Up to this time little has been discovered as to the true structure of the wood of large sigillaria, and nothing whatever is known as to the foliage of the plant. It is true that M. Adolphe Brongniart, as before alluded to, has figured a small specimen of what he terms sigillaria, shewing (sic) most beautiful structure, but this fossil would not be ranked with our large sigillaria by its external characters. Professor William King, of Galway, many years since, stated that the common fern, pecopteris nervosa, would prove to be the foliage of sigillaria, but hitherto little evidence has been offered either in support of or against this opinion.

In this communication no attempt has been made to enter into the question of the internal structure of stigmaria and sigillaria. That of the root is now pretty well known, having been carefully investigated by M. Corda, Mr. Prestwich, F.R.S., and Dr. J. D. Hooker, F.R.S., but the structure of the stem still remains to be worked out. All that has been done is due to M. Adolphe Brongniart, and was made out from the small specimen previously alluded to. At present it may be confidently stated that the central pith of stigmaria, sigillaria, anabathra, and many lepidodendra, (The specimens of small sigillaria resemble some of the lepidodendra so much that it is often hard to determine one genus from the other, and my specimens, shewing pith, are of the small sigillaria, and not the large furrowed kind.)

In conclusion I may affirm that the more I investigate the fauna and flora of our British coal-fields the more I am convinced of their marine character. This view of the case is becoming more and more common every day.

In a discussion after reading the paper, Binney said the first idea of stigmaria being the root of the sigillaria was conceived when he was 15 years of age, and he got it from an old collier. He was determined from that time to work it out, but, after he had discovered the fact, and collected overwhelming evidence on the point, it took six or eight years to make people believe it.

The Leading Features of the Lancashire Coalfield

Joseph Dickinson, F.G.S.
A paper read in September, 1905

The Lancashire coal-field has been described by numerous authors. Many of the monographs appear in the "Transactions of the Manchester Geological (and now Mining) Society. The first two of these in 1839, followed by a third in 1840, were written by that able pioneer and practical geologist, Mr. Edward William Binney, who added many others afterwards. Following on in 1862, came the present writer's first paper, with a detached sheet of sections of the strata, some of which were by eminent mining engineers whose names are duly acknowledged in the text. It would be a long list to specify all the writers. Suffice it to say that in 1904, came one by Mr. Herbert Bolton on the palaeontology, and one on the Bradford (Manchester) part of the coal-field by Mr. John Gerrard.

In 1865, at the request of the Lancashire and Cheshire Coal Association, the present writer gave to the North of England Institute of Mining Engineers, on their visit to Manchester, a short paper on "Some of the Leading Features of the Lancashire Coal-field," which is printed in their Transactions. Being now asked by the Council of the Manchester Geological and Mining Society to give a paper on the same subject to the Institution of Mining Engineers on the occasion of their 1905 visit to Manchester, and since it is superflous to repeat details, what he now proposes is to outline very briefly the 1865 paper, and with additions to endeavour to bring it up to date.

Outline

The maximum thickness of the Carboniferous formation in Lancashire is about 4,850 yards. This consists of: The Coal-measures, about 2150 yards: the Millstone Grit, with accompanying strata, 2,000 yards: and the Mountain Limestone, 700 yards. The coal-field in point of thickness, number of seams and variety of coal, is comparable with the thickest coal-fields of the kingdom.

The Millstone Grit, notably between Burnley and Chatburn, differs very much from the thin representative strata of farewell rocks, shales and conglomerate, as seen on the northern outcrop in South Wales, or as compared with the much thinner representative between Durham and Cumberland. The Mountain Limestone, next below, is more divided into masses with intermediate strata and the usual minor divisional bedding, than the more solid mass in Wales, the division into masses being completed further north.

The outcrops of the coal-field are traceable round the outskirts, the crop of the lower coal-seams being mainly on high ground. These outcrops are not always in parallel lines, but often disconnected and altered by change of dip and faults. The chord-line, across where the coal-field is overlain by unconformable New Red Sandstone, Permian Marls and Permian Sandstone, is usually of low elevation.

Consequently upon the great thickness of the coal-field, it has been found convenient by mining engineers to divide it into three series--the Upper, Middle and Lower. The Upper Series counts from the top down to and including the Worsley and Pendleton Top Four-foot seam. The Middle Series, from the Worsley Four-foot down to and including the Arley seam. The Lower Series from the Arley down to the lowest seam: this Lower Series, from the fact that many of the outcrops are on the hills, is sometimes called the Mountain Mine Series.

The coal in the Upper Series is usually swifter burning than that in the other series - the Worsley Four-foot having long been prized as suitable for bakers' ovens and shortage of boiler-power. Other seams are often known by names corresponding to the special purposes which they suit. Some geologists have demurred to the division of the coal-field into series; but, for ordinary practical purposes, the division is found too convenient to be given up.

In dealing with numerous sections of strata it should be understood that in some the thickness is measured at right angle to the bedding, whilst in others (as in vertical shafts through dipping strata) it is usually measured vertically, which shows more thickness. Consequently, in comparing sections, allowance is required for the difference. And further, actual discrepancies have sometimes to be rectified in sections of shafts and bore-holes which pass through faults, the throw of which causes some strata to be missed and lessens the distance to lower seams; whilst on rare occasions, in contorted strata, a vertical shaft might pass three times through the same seam.

Variations in the Coal Field

Tracing the coal-field from point to point, some strata are found continuing over long distances with few changes, and others changing variously. These variations arise from: - (a) Faults; (b) changes of dip; (c) intervening strata; and (d) variation of the coal seam.

(a) Faults - Faults are the greatest displacements. They are numerous, and the coal has to be worked in belts between them. The largest fault comes through Bolton and by the Irwell valley to Pendleton. At Darcy Lever Hall, the Worsley Top Four-foot coal, at the bottom of the Upper Series, crops out against the downthrow side of the fault, and at the opposite side are the strata near the bottom of the Middle Series, showing a throw of about 1,000 yards, and for 3 miles southwards the Four-foot coal and the strata above it are absent. At Pendleton, where the crops of the Four-foot comes against the upthrow side of the fault, New Red Sandstone and Permian are in at the downthrow side: (from underneath which, about 2 miles northwards, the Four-foot emerges) the difference of distance at the reverse positions being occasioned by difference of dip. This great fault has been cut through, and, as seen by the writer, was found to be of great width, verifying the old observation "the wider the fault-vein the greater the throw."

(b) Changes of Dip - Changes of dip come next in varying the courses. The dip east of Blackburn through Great Harwood is almost vertical, with the summit occasionally turned over in the reverse direction, and different elsewhere. Dips in the interior vary from 1 in 2 to nearly horizontal. Common dips are 1 in 3 and 1 in 5. The overlying unconformable formations usually dip in similar direction with the coal-bearing strata, but generally at a different rate.

(c) Intervening Strata - New beds intervening sometimes occasion change, which, unless followed step by step, is difficult to trace. Sandstone rocks are, perhaps, the most intrusive. With them, as is sometimes said, "the coarser the structure, the shorter the range."

(d) Variations of Coal-seams - Variations of coal-seams are often very important. Dirt-bands come in between the beds of some coal-seams, and occasionally thicken into varied strata, and then further away the coal-beds either re-unite or become dispersed.

The Coal-Measures

Upper Series--The Worsley and Pendleton Top Four-foot seam, at the base of the series, is an instance of long continuance with little change. It has been extensively worked south of the Irwell-valley fault from Bedford,Leigh, through Astley, Worsley, Patricroft and Pendlebury to Pendleton, in the course of which it is crossed by large faults. It has also been worked north of the Irwell-valley fault, from Darcy Lever Hall, ¼ mile north-west of the confluence of the Croal and the Irwell to 2½ miles eastwards. Instances of change in this Upper Series are given in part V of this paper, on the Manchester portion of the coal-field, in which the correlation of this Four foot seam has long been debatable.

Middle Series--In the Middle Series are many changes, of which the following are some, in descending order:

The Ince and Gidlow group of coal-seams at Wigan become the Binn, Shuttle, Crumbouke, Brassy and the Rams eastwards. In this course, the seam now generally called the Rams, has been and is still occasionally known as the Seven-foot and the Six foot. At Clifton, the Shuttle and Crumbouke lie 15 yards apart: at Great Lever, Little Lever and Radcliffe, they are united and form the Upper Three Yard. The Brassy seam between the Crumbouke and the Rams, entirely disappears between Clifton and Pendlebury colliery, being replaced by sandstone-rock; and in the same range, the top coal of the Rams disappears.

The Pemberton Five-foot, Two-foot and Four-foot, respectively 12 and 15 yards apart at Wigan, maintain about the same lie as far as Haydock where they are named the Florida, but at St. Helens they become apparently the Higher and Lower main delf, only 4 yards apart. East of Wigan, at Abram, Westleigh, Tyldesley and Shakerley, the Two-foot and Four-foot are united as the Great Seven-foot; farther east, separation sets in, so that at Worsley, Kersley, Clifton and Pendlebury they are the White and Black seams, 30 yards apart. Near Bolton, the beds are united as the Lower Three-yard or Ten-foot, which continues until the lower part separates into a distinct seam called the Gingham: the Ten Foot above holding on. Farther east, at Radcliffe Bridge, the beds become so separated as to have as yet been little worked.

The well-known Wigan Cannel coal (now represented mainly by exhausted workings) and the King coal-seam below, undergo many changes. Elsewhere, the Cannel disappears, and is often replaced by ordinary coal, with the King coal diverging, as at Westhoughton, to 17 yards or so, and becoming known as the Sapling. Farther away, at Stoneclough, Clifton, Ainsworth, Radcliffe and Elton, with sometimes a trace of cannel on the top, the seam has been extensively worked. At Elton, it becomes known as the Hynes mine, with the Sapling coming close up near Bury. Then, beyond a large vacant area, at Middleton, the seams are usually considered to correlate with the Bent mines united, and at Oldham as the Upper and Lower Bent seams, and at Ashton-under-Lyne as the Two-foot and Peacock, about 20 yards apart.

The Wigan Plodder, Yard, Half-yard, Three-quarter, and the Arley group are the lowest seams of the Middle Series. The Yard and the Arley have been extensively worked, the others partially. Most of these seams thin eastwards, some disappear, and, north of the Irwell-valley fault, they are almost entirely unrecognized. At Elton and Bury, a coarse thick seam called the Dogshaw appears (after a few traces), and has been worked. The Dogshaw from its position has been assumed to be the Arley; but, from other associations, it seems more likely to be the Plodder revived. Beyond Bury, the entire Middle Series disappears for some distance. A seam reappears in similar position at Rochdale, Heywood, and other detached places, and is called the Royley, where the main coal-field crops out east of Oldham and Ashton-under-Lyne.

In the Burnley part of the coal-field, where the Middle Series reappears, the lowest seam in the series was formerly called a Four-foot, but latterly for distinction has been called the Arley. A shell-bed, with remarkably large fossil shells, long called Anthracosia (but now seemingly referred to as Anthracomya or Carbonicola robusta), lies a few yards above the Arley mine at Wigan and in the vicinity.

Lower Series--In the Lower Series, variations occur similar to those described in the Upper and Middle Series. Several of them are mentioned in the writer's former papers, and need not be repeated here. Suffice it to mention the change in position between the Upper Foot and the Gannister coal-seams. For a long range north-east of Oldham, these two seams lie about 15 yards apart. In the Upper Foot coal are spherical concretions, called "bullions," and in the roof over the coal are lenticular cakes containing numerous fossil shells (Goniatites, etc.) and some vegetable matter. When struck, these cakes emit an odour like garlic.

The water from the coal, etc., yields much ochre, and, like nitric acid, it temporarily discolours a person's skin. Near Portsmouth (Cliviger), and Tooter Hill (Bacup), and notably Wholaw old colliery (3 miles south of Burnley), where the writer has seen the transition, the Upper Foot dips steeply down and unites with the Gannister coal. The two seams continue united as the Gannister Four-foot through the Burnley part of the coalfield to Colne, with the same characteristics continuing as those appertaining to the Foot before the union. The same kind of fossils also appear with the seam at Ingleton in Yorkshire, amd are of great diagnostic value. At Wholaw, where the seams unite, the floor contains masses of iron-pyrites.

It is only the Lower Series which connects the Burnley part with the main coal-field. It is an improving series northwards, appearing ultimately, in greatly expanded form, as the great Durham and Northumberland coal-field.

Manchester Portion of the Coal-field

The Manchester portion of the Lancashire coal-field requires special mention. It is surrounded by the large faults and unconformable New Red Sandstone and Permian. As it is thus isolated from the main coal-field, with the strata varied and different nomenclature of seams, diverse opinions have long been held on the correlation. The debates have centred chiefly on the question whether the Bradford (Manchester) Four-foot coal is identical with the Worsley and Pendleton Top Four-foot.

In 1879, Mr. Clegg Livesey, one of the old firm of owners of the Bradford colliery, in giving the section of strata of the Parker pit to the Manchester Geological Society, stated that formerly the firm supposed the Bradford Four-foot to lie about 300 yards above the Pendleton Crumbouke and Rams group of seams, but that after many explorations, one a shaft extending through the Bradford Four-foot at 110 yards to a thick rock and then by bore-hole to a total depth of 700 yards, they failed to find the Crumbouke and Rams series, the best seam met with being at 550 yards and that only about 3 feet in thickness, which they had named the Parker after the lord of the manor, and were working.

Since the decease of Mr. Livesey, the present owners of the Bradford colliery have extended the explorations to nearly 350 yards below the Parker mine, where they have found coal to which they are sinking, and expect to reach it by a shaft at a depth of about 900 yards below the surface. A cross-measure drift, dipping steeply across the strata, which dip at the rate of about 1 in 3, has already reached the coal, and the shaft has passed through the Parker.

The continous section thus proved at Manchester consists of:

		Yards
Ardwick Limestone, in twelve beds (24 ft 10 in)		157
Coal-measures cropping out to top of Bradford shafts		330
	Yards	
Bradford shafts to Bradford Four-foot	110	
Bradford shafts below Bradford Four-foot to Parker	440	
Bradford drift, below Parker seam to coal	350	900
Total thickness proved		1387

The principal beds of the Ardwick Limestone have been worked extensively. The mines are now closed, and the deep shaft is used as a pumping station; and it seems desirable therefore, to repeat the section furnished several years ago by Mr. William Mellor, who managed the mines for many years.

Section of the Ardwick Limestone Strata, Manchester

Commencing (under 4 feet 6 inches of marl) below the Permian Sandstone

	Thickness		Total Thickness	
First Limestone	1	2	1	2
Dark clay floor, 8 in red clay, 10 ft	10	8	11	10
Second Limestone, with open joints	1	4	13	2
Grey clay-floor, 6 inches clay, 11 ft	11	6	24	8
Third Limestone	1	4	26	0
Hard red clay	13	6	39	6
Fourth Limestone	0	10	40	4
Very hard red clay	36	0	76	4
Fifth Limestone	1	0	77	4
Grey and Red clays	24	0	101	4
Sixth Limestone	2	0	103	4
Clay, 23 ft; grit-stone, 1 foot; gritty shale, 21 ft; clays 54 ft	99	0	202	4
Seventh Limestone	4	0	206	4
Red and green shale beds	15	0	221	4
Eighth Limestone	3	0	224	4
Red and Green clays	4	0	228	4
Ninth Limestone (occasional)	1	0	229	4
Clays and shales, with calcerous courses	15	0	244	4
Tenth Limestone	1	6	245	10
Shales and grits, 45 feet: coal and blackband iron-stone, 1 foot 6 ins: sandy shale 6 feet	52	6	298	4
Eleventh Limestone, main seam in 6 beds, limestone, 5 ft 4 ins: shale 3 ft 8 ins	9	0	307	4
Red, etc., shale 60 ft, COAL, 6 inches: floor 6ft	66	6	373	10
Large calcerous nodules	0	10	374	8
Shale Holt Town sandstone, 81 ft: red shale, 15 ft	96	0	470	8
Twelth Limestone and red iron	2	0	472	8

Some of the limestone is of brecciated structure. The lime produced has the property of a slowly-setting cement, which for many years was highly valued as the best for bricking in colliery-shafts.

The colliery-workings in the Manchester portion have extended from near the river Irk (partly under the slope of St. Georges's fault, Rochdale Road), to beyond Belle Vue, Hyde Road, a distance of 3 miles on the level course. Several seams of coal have been worked, most of them thin: The Openshaw seam, to a small extent, chiefly for fire-clay: the Charlotte, Three-quarter, Four-foot, Yard and Parker: also a little of the New, the Doctor, and Two-foot, which lie between the Yard and the Parker. A thin coal and fire-clay have also been mined to a small extent at Hendon Vale, Smedley, in the Valley of the Irk.

Most of the workings were closed before the 1872 Coal-mines Regulation Act first made the deposit of record-plans obligatory. This requirement, now continued by the 1887 Continuing Act, makes such deposits private for 10 years, except with the owner's consent. But under the 1896 Act, view is allowed for purposes of safety, with the consent of the Secretary of State. Consequently, plans of the earlier working were not so deposited. But the plan of the Bradford Four-foot was so deposited, and 10 years having expired, it is free to be viewed at the Home Office, Whitehall, London. The plan throws much light on this part of the coal-field: and it is an instructive record of how the extensive dip-workings were won underneath the dead water of former workings, and how in parts of deep workings pillars (40 yards wide and 20 yards workings between) were considered best for surface-support.

Strangers viewing this plan of the Four-foot mine may wonder what stopped the extension of the workings northwards to St. George's fault. The reason is said to be one of the cautions against disposing of property in small holdings without reserving the minerals.

As to the correlation of the strata of the Manchester part of the coal-field with the strata at Pendleton, it may be thought an easy task, having about 1,387 yards for the comparison. The writer of this paper has long known the upper part of the section. Now he has been kindly made acquainted with the lower portion. Yet throughout the whole, the division of seams precluded hasty identification. The additional evidence appears to strengthen the view that the Bradford (Manchester) Four-foot coal-seam is identical with the Pendleton and Worsley Top Four-foot.

The difficulty of reconciling this view has all along been the absence, from the Bradford strata, of seams of coal corresponding with those that occur in the Rams group west of Manchester. Actual proof is still wanting. In endeavouring to explain this want, the writer is forced to the conclusion that, at Bradford, important portions of this group have become displaced by the thick sandstone-rock, 300 yards below the Four-foot coal. He describes, in part IV. of this paper, the proved displacement at Pendlebury of the whole of the Brassy seam from this

160

group by intervention of sandstone-rock. Apparently, therefore, the displacement is increased at Bradford. As to the lower seams at Bradford, the Parker, (a white-ash coal) probably accords with the White coal of the Pemberton group: and the deeper seams in varied form accord with seams in lower groups.

As to the correlation with seams east of Manchester, the Pendleton Shuttle and Crumbouke and the Three-yard of Radcliffe (of the Rams group) apparently accord with the Staneley seam at Moston and the Roger at Ashton-under-Lyne. Mention has recently been made of the discovery in the new shaft at Bradford, of a bed of limestone 1 foot thick containing the small Spirortis, between the Bradford Three-quarter and Four-foot seams, usually of diagnostic value: but since no corresponding stratum has yet been noticed either at Pendleton or Patricroft, west of Manchester, this find does not help the correlation.

The Overlying New Red Sandstone and Permian

At the time when the 1865 paper was written, the New Red Sandstone and Permians overlying the Lancashire coal-field were often grouped by mining engineers as the "red-rock". Since then, the distinctions have become generally recognized, although some changes have occurred from time to time, even in high quarter, on the acquisition of matured information. The Ardwick Limestone, overlying the Manchester portion of the coal-field, was once classed sometimes, with the part of the Magnesian Limestone; but the two thin coal seams and fossils cause it at present to be classed with the Coal Measures.

The Manchester "red rock" of old is now generally divided into:

New Red Sandstone, with pebbles in the lower portion: say, about 400 yards.

Permian Marls, the lower portion with numerous thin fossiliferous limestones in beds and lenticular cakes; and, at the bottom, a bed of conglomerate about 3 feet thick, total, 60 to 86 yards: say, 70 yards.

Permian Sandstone, soft, part being good moulding-sand. Bored through at Droylesden, 250 yards, and at Heaton Park 278 yards: say 270 yards.

The New Red Sandstone and the Permians, although thrown by the same large faults, are unconformable with the coal-strata. The rates of dip are different and so are the positions of the coal bearing strata where the covering comes on. At Ardwick (Manchester), the Permian Sandstone comes on almost close above the highest proved bed of Ardwick Limestone; and (including the 157 yards of Ardwick Limestone) about 600 yards above the Bradford (Manchester) Four-foot coal. At Patricroft abandoned colliery, the Permian Marls come on at about 350 yards above the Worsley and Pendleton Top Four-foot. Thus assuming the Bradford Four Foot to correlate with this seam, this implies a decrease westward of 250 yards in 6 miles, and the ratio continues. At Nook pits, Astley, near Tyldesley, 5 miles farther west, it is only about 113 yards above the same Four-foot: a decrease of 237 yards in 5 miles. At Milner's abandoned colliery, a mile still farther west, it is about 90 yards, a decrease of 23 yards. The average decrease (510 yards in 12 miles) is above 42 yards per mile. Farther west yet, at Plank Lane colliery (Westleigh), and at Maypole (Abram), the Four-foot seam cease to crop out, being covered by the New Red Sandstone and Permian.

Water is pumped in large quantities from the New Red Sandstone, Permian and Coal-measure sandstones; and deeper wells sometimes drain the shallower. When Mr. Thomas Livesey's trial-shaft entered the thick Coal-measure sandstone, it drained the Newton Heath brewery-well, which continued whilst the shaft was unwatered. Contrarywise, when the Droylesden bore-hole was in the Permian Sandstone, 110 feet below sea-level, all the water to that depth went away and sand was washed with it; and when boring ceased at a depth of 1,300 feet, the bottom part was puddled, to assist in preventing water from passing down into future workings.

Pumping stations in watery New Red Sandstone and Permian, overlying colliery-workings, require watching lest the well might be deepened and thus flood the colliery. This applies especially where working unknown to the well-owner are under the slope of a fault. For many years past, a continuous barrier of coal has been left against the overhanging Irwell-valley fault.

Conclusion

The general outline of the coal-field is semi-circular, with unconformable New Red Sandstone and Permian at the chord, under which it dips, to re-emerge on the opposite side of the basin in North Staffordshire, North Wales, and the Wirral peninsula. It is dislocated by large faults, altered by dips, change of strata, including coal-seams. Each fault, as usual, slopes towards the downthrow side at an obtuse angle from the bedding of the strata, no matter how the strata dip.

The largest fault has corresponding strata, 1,000 yards higher at one side than at the other side: but the surface of the ground is levelled off to the same altitude at both sides, similarly to other faults. Over this levelled-off surface, there is ordinarily, up to a certain elevation, a covering of drift composed of clay, sand and pebbles, dragged or conveyed from distant outcrops, the whole lying unconformably upon the strata beneath. These disappearances of strata from the upthrow side of faults, and the disappearance of very much larger masses of ground shown by vacancies, are accounted for geologically by imaginary denudation and ice-flows.

Vast areas of the best coal-seams at moderate depths have been worked: some entirely, leaving the vacant goaf compressed between the roof and floor of the mine: and some with pillars of coal, varying from one-fourth to two-thirds of the whole, left purposely for surface-support. Workings have already attained a depth exceeding 1,160 yards below the surface.

Places for new winnings within the area of the coal-field proper are few and difficult to find: thus, forcing an increasing number of sinkings to pierce the overlying watery formations on the dip. Possibly the first surprise of the intelligent mining engineering-visitor from comparatively faultless coal-fields may be to find that, among such large dislocations, coal is produced from between the belts as cheaply as in many other districts.

The Anderton Shearer Loader

by L.C. Timms, B.Sc., Member and T.Lester
Area Production Manager, and Area Mechanisation Engineer,
respectively
No. 3 (St.Helens) Area, North Western Division, N.C.B.

A paper read in January, 1955

Synopsis

The paper describes the features of the Anderton Shearer Loader and the experience gained from all installations under a variety of conditions in the St.Helens Area. The average face O.M.S. from all these installations is nearly 6 tons, which is approximately double the average face O.M.S. from faces worked by conventional methods.

One installation is described in detail with notes on the special features of the other installations.

The effects of shearer loading on the size of product, roof control and on the consumption of explosives are dealt with in detail. The experience has been that unless the whole working section is cut out, there is an average reduction of 3 to 4% in large coal over 3 in., an increase of 1 to 2% in fines and an increase in the intermediate sizes.

Roof conditions show a marked improvement on the power-loaded faces.

Introduction

Mining conditions in the St. Helens Area have always been difficult. Previous generations of mining engineers have had to contend with average gradients of 1 in 4: outbursts and heavy emissions of methane: major faults: and a heavy concentration of local faulting, together with the interaction of multiple-seam workings in constricted takes. Added to all these difficulties the present generation had to grapple more and more intimately with the problem of exhaustion of reserves, often necessitating the working of thinner and more difficult seams.

Since Vesting Date the aim has had to be towards concentration of output and all Production Officials have been busily engaged in effecting much needed improvements in haulage arrangements, pit-bottoms, pit-top circuits, the layout of districts and the constant search for extended reserves. At all collieries there has been some improvement in the capital investment depending on the expectation of life at each of the pits.

The net result, comparing 1953 with 1947, has been an increase of 17.7% in gross output, 14.2% in saleable output, and 17.4% in overall O.M.S. bringing this to 20.9 cwt (saleable). For the last two or three years, however, the rate of improvement has been slowing down and it became obvious that continued improvement could only spring from a material increase in face efficiency. Hitherto it had been generally considered that the physical conditions in this Area were totally unsuitable for armoured conveyors and power loading: yet it was becoming plain that unless face efficiency could be improved the results would not merely remain low but would deteriorate, as the physical conditions were not likely to improve with the passing of time.

A critical examination was made of all the power-loaders available and expert advice was sought on the suitability of the best faces in the Area for power loading. Each time there was some factor which could be raised as an objection to an installation being tried. It may be the floor was too soft, the seam height too variable or the coal too hard, needing pre-cutting, and in every case there was the ever-present boggy – local faulting.

It soon became evident that none of the power-loaders then available could have more than a very local and fleeting effect on the Area results. Something new was required: a machine which was independent of roof or floor, small and easily manoeuvrable at faults and capable of giving a steady continuous flow of coal to the haulages, of limited capacity, which fed many of the districts in the Area. The Area General Manager, Mr. J. Anderton, set out to find a solution to these problems.

The immediate object was to turn a coal cutter on its side and mount it on an armoured conveyor, so that the plane of the cut was vertical and a web of coal about 1 foot thick was taken off. The jib could easily be adjusted to trim the floor and, by adding another trailing jib, the roof coal could be trimmed down in the seam of varying thickness.

This was tried successfully in a seam 6ft thick, but was rather cumbersome. The demand for simplicity soon led to the use of a disc in place of the jibs.

Description of Anderton Shearer Loader

The basic design of the shearer loader is similar to that of a coal cutter, being rather like a disc coal cutter with the disc operating vertically instead of horizontally and travelling on a Panzer conveyor.

166

The Gearhead

This section of the machine was orginally adapted to take a gearbox to provide a horizontal shaft for the discs. This adaptation has worked very satisfactorily except that it cannot operate in seams less than 3ft 8in thick. A shallow type of gearhead had now been designed in the Area to replace completely the original design. This enables the shearer loader to be introduced into seams having a total height of 2ft 9 in., which considerably widens the application of the machine.

The Haulage Unit

The haulage section of the machine has so far been that of a normal coal cutter slightly modified. The modifications include a deeper drum fitted with segments to convert into a Clifton wheel, so that the machine can haul itself along a dead-rope running the full length of the face. The gear ratios have also been altered to give higher travelling speeds than those normally used on coal cutters. Cutting speeds of up to 10 ft per min and flitting speeds up to 80ft per min are now in use. It is expected that in the very near future hydraulic haulage units will be available which will give an infinitely variable rate of travel from zero to 40ft per min. This method of propelling a machine will provide a transmission system free from the high shock-loading which is at present experienced with the ratchet and pawl system, and a reliable system of relief at a pre-determined rope load can be incorporated.

Power Unit

Most of the shearer loaders in operation in the St. Helens Area are powered by 50 h.p. motors and generally good results are being obtained without a serious rise in temperature. In the few cases where power requirements have been abnormal due to hardness of coal or height or depth of shear, 70 h.p. motors have been used. It is interesting to compare the power requirements of a normal coal cutter with those of a shearer loader. A test was made on a coal cutter fitted with a jib giving an effective depth of cut of 4ft. 6in. with a 6in. kerf (2½ sq. ft. face area), the cutting position being at a height of 2ft 6in from the floor level. This machine absorbed an average of 35 h.p. at a speed of 5ft per min. A shearer loader operating on the same face and taking a 16in. x 40in. shear (7sq. ft. face area) required an average of 40 h.p. at a speed of 7 ft. per min. The motors in each case were of the same manufacture and specification. At the relative travelling speeds quoted, the amount of coal being removed per minute as 11.2 cu. ft. by the coal cutter compared with 31.1 cu. ft. by the shearer.

167

One of the reasons why the shearer power demands are relatively low is the complete absence of friction between the main driving shaft and the picks. The friction between a cutting chain and a jib can never be correctly assessed at it varies, not only with the resistance offered to the pick points but also with the characteristics of the dust between the chain and the jib race.

The Discs or Drum

The shearing medium may consist either of a series of discs or a drum. The discs are employed as carriers for the pick holders which are set at varying angles to provide a pre-determined number of pick lines. Pick lacing and the number of lines of picks are all important and many experiments have been made by varying the lacing of the picks and the number of lines. It has been found that the normal protrusion of up to 2 in. is not sufficient in some cases to prevent the pick holders from rubbing on the solid coal. The normal remedy would be to introduce more lines of picks but this would require an increase in the number of discs, or alternatively, the use of pick holders with wider angles, which would call for more power due to the sides of the pick holders rubbing on the coal.

With a view to eliminating picks set at an angle, a drum was designed which allowed better lacing and an arrangement of lines of picks to give more efficient shearing. All the picks are set at right angles to the drum with the exception of the outer picks, which have been set at an angle to provide clearance for the drum sides.

With the new drum the picks have a greater protrusion in order to reduce the possibility of pick holders rubbing on the coal and to enable the picks to penetrate up to 3 in., so producing larger coal with less power consumption. Normal cutter picks have shanks measuring approximately 1 in. x ½ in. compared with 1¼ in. x ¾ in. shanks on picks used in the new drum.

Height and Depth of Shear

Most of the shearer loaders in the Area are fitted with discs or drums having a diameter over the picks of 40 in. This gives a reasonable clearance for stable coal to pass under the body of the machine; further, in many seams the top coal will fall without shotfiring after the coal has been undermined to a height of 40 in. and this should be the aim. The smallest diameter of disc used so far is 32 in. and the largest 54 in.

With the shallow-type gearhead it is possible to fit a minimum diameter of disc or drum of 30 in., although the clearance between the

168

Panzer and the body of the machine is then very small. Probably the best way of deciding the height of the shear is as follows:

(a) If the seam height is between 32 and 34 in., a drum diameter of 30 in. is necessary to provide clearance between the roof bars and the machine body.

(b) In conditions where it is imperative to leave coal to form a roof and there are no convenient partings, a drum size equal to the section to be extracted will, in many cases, be satisfactory.

(c) Strong bands of coal or dirt which, if not removed, will prevent the top coal from falling should be removed by the shearer if possible.

(a) and (b) are quite straightforward but there are many variations possible under (c).

Where hard or tough bands exist the height of shear should be at least 2 in. above the band to allow the picks to break through into a softer substance. This usually has the effect of tearing out the hard band in sizeable pieces, so reducing the pick wear and power consumption.

The aim in the St. Helens Area has always been to obtain as fast a shearing speed as possible, for with a fixed speed or rotation the higher the travelling speed the larger the product. If the coal to be sheared is reasonably friable, a 50 h.p. motor is quite capable of taking a 40 in. dia. shear to a depth of 20 in. at a speed of approximately 7 ft. per min. and a reasonable size of product will be obtained. If the coal is tough or "woody" it may be advisable to reduce the depth of shear to 18 in. to obtain the necessary travelling speed without overloading the motor.

On faces advancing on the strike, a 20 in. cut has been found satisfactory without upsetting the stability of the machine. When advancing to the dip the depth of cut may need to be reduced to maintain stability and conversely when advancing to the rise the depth may be increased. As would be expected when shearing against a gradient and when advancing to the rise, the plough transfers the sheared coal to the conveyor much more effectively than in level conditions. In this Area the depths of shear have varied from 15¾ in. to 20 in.

Disc Shaft – Angle of Lag

The first experimental machine had a 15′ angle of lag on the disc shaft which inclined the discs towards the conveyor at the back end of the machine. The object was to throw as much coal as possible on the conveyor and to eliminate grooving in hard floors. This proved unsatisfactory because the wedge of coal between the leading edge of the inner disc and the machine body often fouled the disc shaft and

169

stopped the machine. The first modification consisted of halving the angle of lag to 7½' and this made a great improvement, but in a very strong coal a wedge still persisted. Machines have since been tried with no lag and are giving satisfactory results.

Direction and Rotation of Discs

The normal direction of rotation is such that the coal is thrown over discs on to the deflector plate. This ensures the minimum degradation of the coal. In one case, where the face was advancing to a slight dip, difficulty was experienced in keeping the machine on the Panzer conveyor; by reversing the direction of rotation of the discs this trouble disappeared.

Pick Design

In the experimental stage of the shearer loader a normal type of tool steel pick was used and gave reasonable results in friable coal. It was necessary, however, to change the picks at least after every cycle and it was decided to employ picks having a tungsten carbide tip. The results were very diappointing, for it was found that not only had the power consumption increased but the machine had become unstable. By examining all the picks and watching the machine at work it was found that the shape of the pick was responsible for the unsatisfactory results. It was quite obvious that the blunt attacking portion of the pick was causing friction which accounted for the increased power consumption and instability of the machine.

Mechanical engineers are apt to compare the shearer loader with a milling machine and the early types of tungsten carbide tipped picks were designed accordingly. The action required is very different from milling, for a splitting and plucking action is necessary which calls for a tool well backed-off below the tip to allow the pick to penetrate and split the coal. The pick shank has been altered considerably by backing off and by introducing a positive buttress to provide greater strength to support the tip. The new pick for the drum has been designed to give adequate support for the tip but backed off sufficiently to prevent unnecessary friction.

The Deflector Plough

In the early stages of the experiment an attempt was made to plough coal both during shearing and flitting. It was soon found, however, that while ploughing during flitting was quite satisfactory it was impossible to plough during shearing because the discs became choked with coal. A combined deflector and plough was then devised and this has been found very satisfactory.

The shearing medium and the deflector plough can be likened to an ordinary plough share from which the front portion has been removed and replaced by the discs or drum. The coal removed by the discs or drum is deposited on the deflector plate which, due to its steep angle, acts as a chute for the coal to the conveyor. When the machine is flitting in reverse the opposite end of the deflector plough acts as a normal plough to lift loose coal from the floor and transfer it on to the conveyor. The deflector plough is permanently connected to the underframe of the machine by a link and pins which provide a rugged but flexible connexion (sic).

Dust Suppression

There have been many experiments with dust suppression on shearer loaders but to date the most satisfactory method had been to supply water through a series of jets in the deflector portion of the plough, with the jets of water impinging on the picks before they attack the coal. In addition two mist sprays are fitted on the gearhear so that the mist blankets the coal as it is deposited on to the deflector plate. It is extremely important that there should be adequate pressure for the jets, as it has been found that with a pressure of less than 150 psi the jets may become blocked and so cause a deterioration in the dust suppression.

Cable Carrier

The cable carrier merely consists of a platform suitably guided for travelling on top of the Panzer conveyor and is attached to the shearer loader underframe by a link and two pins. On top of the platform are a series of uprights which act as retainers for the cable. As the machine travels along the face the cable is coiled on to the cable carrier in a figure of 8, which enables the maximum length to be coiled in a given space and does not cause cork-screwing of the cable.

Method of using Anderton Shearer Loader

The following is a description of an installation of a shearer loader at Ravenhead Colliery in the Rushy Park Seam. This is typical of all the installations in the Area and was, incidentally, the first to be introduced in July 1952.

Particulars of No.1 Face, Rushy Park Seam

Roof .... 6ft-12ft medium shale overlain by rock
Coal section .... 3 ft 10 in 4 ft 1 in
Floor .... Medium fireclay, uneven
Length of face .... 150 yards
Gradient on face line .... 1 in 6
Number of roadways to face 4
Thickness of cover .... 850 yards
Distance from shaft .... 3,700 yards

Details of Equipment

Shearer loader .... Converted A.B.15 in. coal cutter,
16in x 40in shear discs
Panzer conveyor .... Westfalia Lunen P.F.1-40 h.p. drive
at each end of the conveyor
Push jacks .... Dollery & Palmer, compressed air, Mk III
Gate conveyors .... Cowlishaw Walker 20 in composite chain
conveyor. Sutcliffe 30 in Goliath gate belt.
C.W. 20 in chain coveyor to loading point
Props .... Dowty hydralic, 48/.14
Bars .... Procar 800 mm link bars

Deployment of Men on No.1 Rushy Park Face

Shearer loader, including cable handling 2
Shothole driller (on back shift) 1
Supports and snaking Panzer 6
Stables 4
Conveyor attendant 1
Shotfirer 1
Maintenance 1
Total 16

Seventeen other face workers are employed on ripping the four gate roads and strip packing, which are normal operations and are common to conventional and power-loading methods.

The system of roof supports adopted is the straight-line type, with props and bars 3ft apart along the face. The propping system includes double propping the bars next to the face to give the maximum resistance possible at this point. The double propping also has the advantage that it holds the bar securely when a cantilever bar is in position.

172

Originally props and bars were set at 4 ft. intervals along the face but roof control was not ideal until the system was altered to 3 ft intervals, and this is now standard on all the prop-free front faces in the Area.

Sequence of Operations

Starting with the shearer loader in the bottom or left-hand stable, shearing commences cutting uphill. The machine operator switches on the motor, sets the travel control and adjusts the water supply for dust suppression.

As the switchgear is in a middle gate road the assistant coils the machine cable in a figure of 8 on the cable carrier during the first half of the shear and uncoils the cable during the second half, replacing the cable on the brackets attached to the Panzer conveyor spill-plates. Provided that the Panzer conveyor is not stopped, the shearer may operate continuously throughout the full face length. When the shearer reaches the top right-hand stable the disc shaft is disengaged, the flitting gear (60ft per min) is engaged and ploughing commences. Usually the return or ploughing journey can be started immediately the cutting journey is completed, but on some faces it may first be necessary to complete the dropping of sticky tops. It is not normally possible for the machine to plough continuously at full speed mainly because the Panzer is not capable of carrying the amount of coal obtained, so the friction clutch is disengaged and re-engaged to suit the carrying capacity of the conveyor.

Whilst the machine is ploughing, the Panzer drive in the top stable is pushed forward and the conveyor snaked towards the bottom stable. Immediately the loader reaches the bottom stable the loose coal pushed by the plough into the stable is cleaned up and the bottom drive is pushed forward.

Propping is being completed during snaking and the loader is now ready to start on the second cycle. The time required to shear, plough and snake the conveyor in readiness for the second cycle on Ravenhead Rushy Park face is normally two hours, but the complete cycle of operations has been completed in one hour forty minutes.

Results from Ravenhead Colliery Rushy Park No 1 District, period 1st January to 30th October, 1954

Number of machine-shifts worked 225.31
Total ouput, raised and weighed .... 52,001 tons
Total number of cycles completed ... 516 (400 mm advance per cycle)

Average number of cycles per shift 2.29
Highest number of cycles in one shift 3.50
Average output per shift .... 230 tons
Highest output in one shift .... 350 tons
Average team O.M.S., raised and weighed .... 15.37 tons
Average face O.M.S., raised and weighed 6.87

Since July, 1952, this installation has worked most consistently, averaging over two cycles per shift. This development unit and face efficiency would be much higher if there were only two roads to the face instead of four.

Maintenance

Maintance on equipment varies according to the conditions under which the equipment is operating but, generally speaking, it is not heavy. On certain machines breakdowns have occurred from time to time, generally in the haulage unit.

Rope life has been found to be satisfactory when using a normal ⅝ in. diameter Langs Lay rope, but better life is obtained with a rope having a steel core in place of the hemp core. The normal flexible cuttier rope is unsatisfactory due to the abnormal stretch plus the flattening of the rope while on the Clifton wheel. Normally rope life is about eighty cycles, which is approximately 13,500 yd of shearing and the same amount of ploughing.

Pick life varies from one set (40) per 3,500 yd to one set per 730 yd. In the latter case pyrites are responsible for the short life.

Apart from such replaceable spares as pawls, ratchet wheels, clutch shafts, and clutches in the haulage unit, the shearer is capable of completing about 300 cycles between overhauls, although certain machines have completed double this figure before a general overhaul became necessary.

The mainenance costs at Ravenhead Colliery are as follows:

Maintenance Costs of the Shearer Loader at Ravenhead Colliery over a period of 27 months

	£
Machine spares and overhauls	1,725
Ropes	215
Picks	980
Total	2,920
Cost per ton	5.7d

Regarding Panzer conveyors, the maintenance costs have proved to be exceedingly light. The conveyor operating at Ravenhead Colliery was the first introduced to the Area and the total requirements have been as follows:

	£
1 Re-wound motor	110
1 Complete conveyor chain and flights after 23 months single shift working	970
3 Repaired ramp chutes	25
12 Fusible plugs for fluid couplings	4
Miscellaneous spares	57
Total	£1,166
Cost per ton	2.26d

Optimum Length of Face

The aim must be to reduce dead-time to the minimum and obviously the longer the face, within reason, the greater the productive time. There are, however, limitations imposed by the length of the Panzer conveyor which can be operated efficiently and the length of face which can be adequately supervised.

It has been the experience in the St. Helens Area that a Panzer conveyor 200 yd long, and fitted with a 45 h.p. motor at each end of the conveyor, will give reliable operation, but if this length is exceeded an additional motor or motors are required which reduce the reliability of the Panzer due to additional stress.

For proper supervision, it is essential that the face be kept to a reasonable length, especially in inclined and thin seams, as a supervisor cannot perform his duties efficiently if the distances to be travelled are too great.

Limiting Conditions for Use of Anderton Shearer loader

Until the shallow-type gearhead was manufactured the shearer loader could not operate in seams having a total section of less than 44 in. The shallow-type machine, with the same size of motor, may be operated in a total height of 32 in. giving adequate clearance under the hinged roof bars, provided the latter have a section of not more than 3 in.

Machines are operating on gradients of 17' on line of face with the Panzer conveying in favour of the load and on 5' with the Panzer conveying against the load. There should be no difficulty in working on gradients steeper than 18', but a Panzer conveyor is not a simple piece of equipment to control on gradients of more than 20'.

On faces travelling to the rise, no difficulty has been experienced on gradients of 14'. Where faces are advancing to the dip, it has been found necessary to reverse the disc or drum rotation to obtain stability on gradients of more than 8'. Although the limit is not yet known, it is estimated that gradients of 15' could be tackled successfully provided the depth of shear is reduced accordingly.

Seams containing pyrites are being successfully sheared, but much depends on the size and density of the bands and whether or not they are continuous.

Faults having a throw of up to 5ft in a 4 ft seam have been successfully negotiated without the floor preparation but if the floor is too hard for the picks to attack, then a shallow stable may be necessary to enable shots to be fired in the floor. The machine would be quite capable of trimming the floor in these conditions to prepare it for the Panzer.

General Experience with the Anderton Shearer Loader

There are at present (November,1954) eleven of the machines at work on production faces in this Area and one on a fully-reserved training face. All installations follow closely the description given earlier but there are special features about some of them which may be of interest.

(1) Wood Colliery--Ince Six Feet Seam

The full section of seam in this case is nearly 8 ft but the upper portion is so dirty as to be worthless. It was decided to work only the bottom 4 ft 2 in., although there was no defined parting near this horizon. Roof forming was necessary and a 4 ft 2 in. dia. disc was used to cut out the full working section (see Fig 4).

The first few cuts were very slow, the 50 h.p. motor was grossly overloaded and required over 100 amp while cutting. Three changes have since taken place and the machine is now working very satisfactorily. Firstly, as the face moved away from the ribside the coal became less "dead"; secondly, the 50 h.p. motor was replaced by a 70 h.p. motor: and thirdly, the pick speed was reduced from 743 to 590 ft per min. The machine can now cut comfortably at 7 ft per min and the load on the motor is well within its capacity. It is producing about 5,000 tons per months (saleable) at a team O.M.S. of over 13 tons and a face O.M.S. of 6 tons (saleable).

As would be expected, there is no large coal produced from this face, but, in anycase, owing to the dirty nature of the seam, all the coal would have to be crushed for washing. The nutty size tests are given later under the heading of "Effect on the Size of the Product."

176

(2) Clock Face Colliery--Wigan Four Feet

This face started up with a disc of 40 in. dia. to take out a working section of 4ft 6 in. The tops were so hard and sticky that they had to be shot down but even then could not be got down to a level horizon. The uneven roof created serious difficulties with the setting of link bars and it was decided to try forming with a 54 in. disc.

The machine is not working satisfactorily with a 70 h.p. motor, and is dealing with over 3,000 tons per month at a team O.M.S. of 10½ tons and a face O.M.S. of 4½ tons (saleable).

(3) Golborne Colliery--Crombouke Seam

This installation was put on a face previously worked by conventional methods. To begin with only the top half of the the 260 yd face was equipped for power loading, the lower half remaining on conventional methods, taking off 4 ft 6 in cuts. Dowty props were used on both sides of the face but under link bars on the power loaded side and under steel straps on the other side.

Prior to the installation the roof conditions were far from perfect, "ley" or following dirt commonly falling in varing thicknesses up to 18 in. Soon after the top half went on to power loading the roof conditions improved considerably, but on the lower half of the face coditions still remained bad. When the lower half went on to power loading the same improvement in roof conditions was experienced as on the top half. The reasons for this improvement are discussed later under the heading of "Roof Control".

This face is providing 7,500 tons saleable per month at a team O.M.S. of 14½ tons and a face O.M.S. of 6½ tons. An interesting feature of the installation is that it yields a slack of much lower ash content than was obtained by conventional methods. This is due to less "ley" and soft floor dirt going out with the coal.

(4) Cronton Colliery--Plodder Seam, 1's East Unit

This was a retreating face in the upper half of a seam 14 ft thick with a two foot dirt band in the middle. The lower section had been worked out, advancing by conventional methods and pneumatically stowed. The retreating face was taken back immediately, using the same roads, and was also pneumatically stowed.

The advantage now was that stable work was considerably reduced and no tipping was necessary. In places where the roof had broken down in the former working of the lower seam, the cavity had been pneumatically stowed and long props sometimes left in. Such timber props were cut up by the machine and did not cause a great deal of trouble.

This experience demonstrated very clearly the efficacy of pneumatic stowing. Apart from the occasional cavities referred to, there was no evidence that 4 ft 6 in. of coal had been removed from the floor prior to the working of the retreating face. Even in the roads no effect at all could be noted until the retreating face got back to the ribside from which the bottom face started. In this vicinity the arches were distorted. This installation produced up to 6,700 tons per month at a face O.M.S. of 9.42 tons (saleable).

(5) Clockface Colliery--Crombouke Seam

This is an example of a double-unit power-loaded face in a heavily-faulted area. The two armoured face conveyors deliver on to a central gate feeder and belt.

The right-hand side is 90 yd and the left-hand side 178 yd long. During October, 1954, there were 17 faults on the face varying in throw from 1 to 5 ft and nearly all of them were on the right-hand side face, yet the face O.M.S. (saleable) was 4.31 tons for the right-hand side and 6.57 tons for the left-hand side face.

Results

The outputs obtained at present are perhaps not as large as some of those achieved by installations of the shearer loader in other parts of the country. This is largely due to the fact that so far all the installations in this Area have, for various reasons, been restricted to single-shift working and the main advantage of a non-cyclic system has therefore not yet been seized. Preparations are now in hand for the installation of machines to work on two shifts and these will come into operation during 1955.

Following the first experimental installation at Ravenhead in July, 1952, two shearer loaders were installed during 1953; one at Cronton and one at Golborne, These were followed up by nine more installations during the first ten months of 1954 and it is anticipated that the total number of machines working will be increased to 25 by the end of 1955. By the end of 1953 5% of the Area output was shearer loaded and this proportion had been increased to over 15% by October, 1954.

For the full benefits of power loading to be reflected proportionally in the overall efficiency of the colliery at which it is installed, the efficiency of the rest of the pit must remain constant or at any rate must not decrease.

At four collieries in this Area where shearer loaders have been installed and conditions have otherwise remained fairly constant or improved slightly, the effect on the colliery results has been as shown in Table 1.

Table 1: Effect of power loading on colliery results

Colliery	Face O.M.S Prior cwt	Face O.M.S Since cwt	Overall O.M.S Prior cwt	Overall O.M.S Since cwt	% of colliery output loaded (%)
Lyme	83	99	23	26	28
Wood	63	73	20	24	18
Golborne..................	66	80	22	26	35
Clock Face................	59	65	19	21	37

At the three other collieries (Sutton Manor, Ravenhead and Cronton), where physical changes drastically affected the remainder of the pit, the overall colliery efficiency has been less than before power loading was introduced but even here power loading had kept the overall efficiency higher than it otherwise would have been.

It is interesting to note from Fig. 5 (not shown - Ed.) the theoretical improvement in the Area face O.M.S. which should be obtained as the proportion of the Area output from power loaded faces is increased. It will be seen that the improvement to be expected is not as great when the percentage of power-loaded coal is increased from 0 to 20% as when it is increased from 20 to 40%. As with all systems of mining, the results obtained from a group of installations varies widely according to the physical conditions and the enthusiasm of both men and officials.

The face O.M.S. varies over the 11 installations from 2.77 to 10.8 tons with an average of 5.8 tons. The worst result from a power-loaded face is very little worse than the average of 2.89 tons from all conventional faces and the average face O.M.S. is twice that of the conventional faces. The effect of power loading so far has been to raise the Area face O.M.S. from 2.89 to 3.12 tons and it is steadily continuing to improve.

Effect on Size of Product

The general effect of power loading is to reduce the proportion of large coal obtained. It is very difficult to determine accurately the effect of the shearer loader on the size of coal produced, since cases have been noted where over the same period the decrease in plus 3 in. sizes has been greater at collieries where no power loading has been introduced than at those now producing one third of their output from shearer loaders.

The sizing with shearer loaders varies with the thickness and friability of the seam and the ease with which any top coal will fall. In one case, where tops of 2ft 6 in. thick fell easily into the machine, the proportion of 3 in. size was higher than that obtained by conventional methods, but where the whole section is cut out the proportion of large coal is negligible.

The general experience in this Area is that compared with conventional methods there is a reduction in large coal of 3 to 4%, an increase in fines of 1 to 2% and an increase in the proportion of the intermediate sizes.

(The paper contains a table, paper 2, of the effect of the shearer loader on coal sizes obtained at Cronton Colliery over a period of twelve months when only 1.87% of the output was shearer loaded compared with the succeeding twelve months when 21.99% of the output was power loaded. It can be seen from the table that the reduction in large coal over 3 in. was 2.8% and that the proportion of washed trebles, 3 in. by 2¼ in., but the singles increased by 1.2%. There was a negligible reduction of 0.2% in fines - Ed.)

Reduction in use of Explosives

In cases where the full section of seam is cut out, the only shots which are required are in the stables and at rippings. At Golborne Colliery, where the tops fall fairly easily and the face which is now power loaded was formerly worked by conventional methods, the effect has been to increase the number of tons of coal per shot from 1.27 to 12.5 tons and the ounces of powder per ton of coal on this face have decreased from 4.7 to 0.63.

There has also been a general improvement in the consumption of explosives used in coal in the Area as the application of power loading has been increased. During the December quarter, 1953, when 5% of the Area output was power loaded, the output of coal per pound of explosive used was 5.29 tons and this figure had improved to 5.35 tons during the September quarter, 1954, when 14% of the Area output was power loaded.

Records

Detailed daily records are kept of the events on each shearer-loaded face, particularly of incidents causing stoppages. A daily graphical record is kept for each machine which shows the time taken for each strip, the time taken for each ploughing or flitting journey and the time and cause of stoppages. An output curve shows the number of tubs filled at any time during the shift and usually this is an almost straight line due to the regular distribution of output throughout the shift with a marked absence of peak loading periods.

Roof Support

The system results in good roof control and in general the roof control on prop-free-front faces is much better than on conventional faces in the Area. It is considered that the improvement is due to the following factors:

(a) A system of link bars ensures more rigid adherence to the specified system.

(b) The prop density is greater and the props are more evenly distributed with the link bar system than when using separate bars.

(c) There is normally far less shotfireing on the power-loaded faces to disturb the roof strata.

(d) The face is advanced in increments of about 20 in. compared with 50 to 60 in. in conventional faces.

(e) Packs and chocks can be kept closer to the face.

Difficulties occasionally arise due to the top coal not falling during each shearing strip. In such cases time may be lost while the tops are being dropped. Sometimes the problem can be overcome by fitting a disc large enough to take out the whole section and in another Area a "piggy-back" overcutter has been attached to the shearer loader.

An experiment is about to be tried in this area of firing the tops on the solid before the shearing shift commences. Hydrobel, fired in water-filled holes which have been infused under pressure, will be used. It is hoped that this will have the effect of loosening the tops sufficiently to make them fall when sheared and will also improve dust suppression.

Dust Suppression

The dust suppression equipment described is normally adequate providing it is properly maintained and used with a water pressure of not less than 150 lb per sq.in. to prevent clogging of the jets. There are cases when no water sprays are required, as at Golborne Colliery, where the face is not wet but the coal contains 8% inherent moisture.

Steps are being taken to further improve dust suppression by water infusion before shearing and by the use of drums in place of discs to increase the size of the cut coal.

Conclusions

The original object, namely to produce a power loader capable of wide application in the difficult conditions in the St. Helens Area, has undoubtedly been achieved and the extent to which it has been adopted in other Areas, Divisions and countries abroad, is ample evidence of the contribution which the Anderton Shearer Loader is making to the extension of power loading.

The reports of the Mechanisation Department of the National Coal Board indicate that in September, 1954, there were twenty-three shearer loaders in use in the country compared with three at the same time in 1953, and that they were producing 7% of the country's power-loaded coal from longwall faces.

Like all innovations the machine eliminates certain problems and creates new ones. It has provided a tangible means of improving O.M.S. in this Area by doubling the normal face O.M.S. wherever it is applied. The combined effects of the machine and the roof support system have greatly improved face conditions generally. The system described is popular with officials and men alike and there is now no question of having to convert anyone to power loading - it is much in demand.

The consumption of explosives has been reduced.

The machine has the advantages of simplicity being, if anything, more simple than a coal cutter and requiring stocks of spares very similar to those carried for ordinary coal cutters. It takes up the floor coal, making it unnecessary for men to go on to the face side of the conveyor, and reduces the possibility of ignition from sparking since the cutting surface is fully ventilated. A steady uniform supply of coal is delivered to the loading point and there usually need be very little dead time when the machine is not either cutting or ploughing.

The problems which have been created and partly but not yet completely overcome and which are common to most forms of power loading, are dust suppression and reduction in the proportion of large coal. Another problem is the dropping of sticky top coal, and the means of overcoming it may vary according to conditions in each particular case.

Comparisons are frequently drawn between cutter loaders which travel slowly and take off a wide web, and those which take off a thinner web and therefore have to travel more quickly. Each has its merits and field of application but in conditions similar to those in the

182

St. Helens Area, where roof control is rendered more difficult by the interaction effects of mult-seam workings and local faulting, it is found better to take the thinner web.

(References in the original paper to various drawings, tables etc., have been ommitted from these extracts. The full paper is recorded in the Transactions of the Institution of Mining Engineers, Volume 114).

Sources and Bibliography

Minutes and Transactions of the Manchester Geological and Mining
    Society.
Transactions of the Institution of Mining Engineers.
Mining Journal.
HM Inspectors of Mines Reports.
Royal Commission on Explosions from Coal Dust in Mines, 1892.
History of the British Coal Industry (Vol 2), by Michael W. Flynn
    assisted by David Stokes (Oxford University Press, 1984).
Science in Victorian Manchester, by Robert H. Kargan (M/c Univ
Press).
Early Years of the Ordnance Survey, by Col. Sir Charles Close
    (David & Charles reprints).
Centenary of a 19th Century Geologist, by James Binney, 1912.
Biography of Capt. Thomas Brown, by J. Wilfrid Jackson
    (Manchester Literary and Philosophical Society) 1944.
Manchester Evening News.
Manchester Guardian.
James Lomax 1857 - 1934, by A. C. Howell (1984).
Manchester Old and New, by W. A. Shaw (Cassell and Company, 1894).
Manchester Faces and Places (1892-99).

The Council of the Manchester Geological and Mining Society Branch
wishes to thank the Institution of Mining Engineers, British Jeffrey
Diamond, Dosco Overseas Engineering, Eickhoff, Gaskell Brothers
(Ashton in Makerfield) and Gullick Dobson, for assistance towards the
cost of publishing "Rich Seams".

Acknowledgements

For advice and assistance, much of it technical, my thanks are due to William Shawcross, William Swift, G. Beetham (Anderson Strathclyde), the Protector Lamp and Lighting Company, Dr. G.J.M. Woodrow, Oldham Batteries, Manchester Central Library, James Hooton, Frank Jones, Norman Jones, James C. Fletcher, the Mitchell Library, Glasgow, and the House of Commons Library. The wealth of mining documents and books in the library at the Salford Mining Museum has been invaluable, and Alan Davies, the Museum Keeper, deserves special mention. My apologies to those whose contributions have been overlooked.

Particular thanks to my wife, Florence, for unstinting help and encouragement.

Printed by Cherry Print, Wakefield, West Yorkshire, England